D0265168

ATLAS OF BACTERIOLOGY

First Edition - - - - - 1947
Reprinted - - - - - - 1952

Printed in Great Britain at The Central Press, Aberdeen

ATLAS OF BACTERIOLOGY

BY

R. CRANSTON LOW
M.D., F.R.C.P.E., F.R.S.E.,

Formerly Bacteriology Department, University of Edinburgh; Consulting Physician to the Skin Department, Royal Infirmary, Edinburgh; Lecturer on Diseases of the Skin, University of Edinburgh

AND

T. C. DODDS
F.I.M.L.T., F.I.B.P., F.R.P.S.,

Laboratory Supervisor to the Department of Pathology, University of Edinburgh; Head of Photomicrography Unit at Department of Pathology, University of Edinburgh.

168 ILLUSTRATIONS
of which 167 *are in Colour.*

E. & S. LIVINGSTONE, LTD.
EDINBURGH & LONDON
1952

PREFACE.

THIS atlas is intended primarily for the medical undergraduate and is meant to be used to illustrate what the student hears in the lectures, sees in the practical class and reads in the text-book. It can be used with any of the standard text-books on Bacteriology. Each figure is accompanied by a short note of the magnification, stain and any special feature which should be noticed. No attempt has been made to describe the characteristics of the organisms. We hope that the pictures will speak for themselves and that a careful study of them will teach the student more than would any long description.

The illustrations are all, except one, in colour and have been made partly from actual colour photographs by the Finlay Process and partly from water-colour drawings whenever it was found impossible to reproduce the condition adequately by photography. Great trouble has been taken to ensure accuracy as regards the exact tone of the colours in each illustration, whether it be a section, film or culture. In every case the size of the organism relative to the size of the tissue cells has also been taken into account. The object has been to produce a picture identical, in every detail, with what the student is expected to see in the practical class. Where several bacteria, *e.g.*, the coliform group, have similar morphological and staining characters, in order to save reduplication, an illustration is not always given of each individual organism. Examples, however, are given of all the main types of pathogenic organisms.

Unexpected technical difficulties arose in connection with the photographing of the naked-eye cultures of bacterial growths especially where the growth was transparent or small in size. In the case of transparent growths the colour of the subjacent medium shone through and was registered on the photographic plate so that the growth was practically invisible. Therefore we have not been able to reproduce as many bacterial cultures as was originally intended. It was found that cultures of fungi, being more opaque and larger, lend themselves better to reproduction. That accounts for the relatively large proportion of fungus cultures compared with the ordinary bacterial growths.

The pictures have been made from freshly prepared specimens, where available, from material in the Bacteriology and Pathology Departments of Edinburgh University and from specimens kindly provided by friends. We express our grateful thanks to Professor T. J. Mackie for the encouragement, critical interest and assistance which he has given us in the preparation of this atlas and also for placing all the resources of his Department at our disposal.

We acknowledge, with gratitude, much help in many ways given by Dr J. P. Duguid and by Messrs Cheyne and C. Smith in the preparation of cultures and media. We are also indebted to Messrs A. Doig and J. Paul of the University Pathology Department, to the former for assistance in staining many of the preparations and to the latter for help with the photographic work.

We have pleasure in recording our indebtedness to Mr J. E. Wilson, Senior Research Officer, Ministry of Agriculture and Fisheries at Lasswade and to Mr R. O. Muir, Research Officer to the same Department, for much help in providing material illustrating animal diseases: We also acknowledge gratefully material provided by Dr van Rooyen, Dr Yusef Akrawi (of Baghdad), Dr W. Levinthal, Bacteriologist to the Royal College of Physicians Laboratory, Dr A. C. P. Campbell of the University Pathology Department, Mr John G. Campbell of the Department of Poultry Diseases, Royal (Dick) Veterinary College, Dr Agnes McGregor and Mr T. McDonald of the Royal Hospital for Sick Children, Mr J. Dick of the Royal Infirmary Bacteriology Laboratory, Mr D. Kay of the Royal Northern Infirmary, Inverness, and Mr J. M. Scouller of the Western Infirmary, Glasgow. We also wish to express our thanks to the Journal of the American Medical Association for kindly permitting us to publish copies of photographs, taken by the electron microscope, from an article by Drs Mudd and Anderson.

Lastly it gives us great pleasure to acknowledge our indebtedness to the publishers, Messrs E. & S. Livingstone for the immense amount of trouble they have taken to meet our very exacting wishes in many directions in the production of this atlas.

R. CRANSTON LOW.

T. C. DODDS.

EDINBURGH UNIVERSITY,
MAY, 1947.

INTRODUCTION.

In compiling this Atlas a definite system has been adopted. Each group of organisms is dealt with separately and in each group the illustrations are arranged in the following order:

1. Clinical material, such as pus, urine, blood, sputum, etc., showing the organism.
2. Culture-film of the organism stained by Gram or other special stain to show special features, *e.g.*, capsule or flagella.
3. Sections of tissue to show the relation of the organism to the tissues.
4. Cultures in Petri dish or test-tube on the medium usually used for each organism.

When looking at each figure the first things the student requires to know are the magnification and staining method used. These have therefore been placed first. In most cases the organism is represented under the oil-immersion lens at 1000 diameters but when dealing with very small organisms, *e.g.*, viruses, a higher magnification is used and for larger organisms, *e.g.*, fungi, a lesser magnification (50-500 diameters) is employed. In all cases the size of the organism, compared with the size of the tissue cells, has been carefully measured, the human red blood corpuscle (diameter 7 μ) being used as the standard of comparison.

The culture tubes are reproduced actual size as also are some of the isolated colonies in plate cultures but, as some of the latter were found to be too small to portray easily in their actual size, they have been enlarged from 5 to 15 times and the picture given is that seen by artificial light under a hand lens or plate-culture microscope.

The student is recommended to study each picture slowly and carefully. A rapid cursory glance will not reveal the details. Only a prolonged inspection will enable all the points to be appreciated. Each picture should be looked at, for some minutes and on repeated occasions, till a permanent impression has been gained.

STAPHYLOCOCCI

Differentiate between Pathogens and Non pathogens.

1. Gram +ve
2. Pathogenicity tests :- a) Mannite ferment^n
b) Gelatine liquefact: (proteolytic)
c) Coagulase production
d) Haemolysins

Coagulase negative Staphs are non pathogenic.

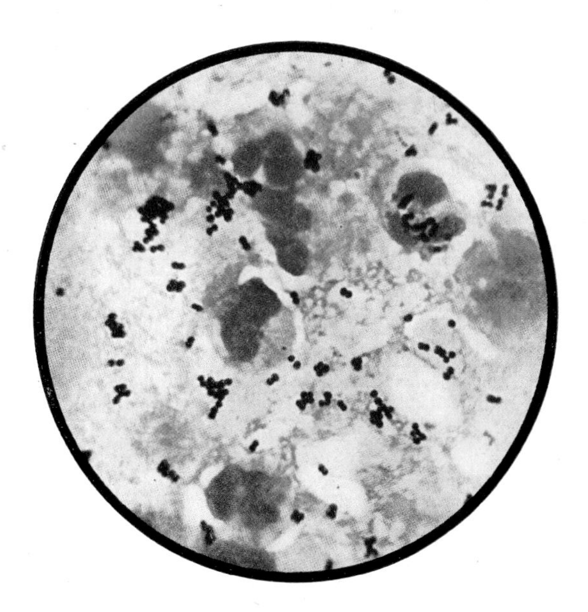

FIG. 1.

× **1000.** *Gram's stain.*

Film of pus from abscess showing **Staphylococcus pyogenes**—a spherical Gram-positive coccus in irregular clusters which are characteristic. Single organisms, pairs and short chains of three or four are also seen.

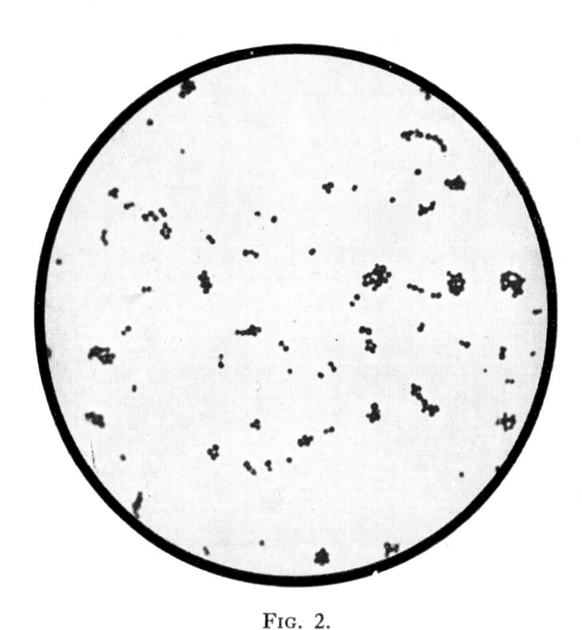

FIG. 2.

× **1000.** *Gram's stain.*

Film of 18 hour culture of **Staphylococcus pyogenes aureus** in broth showing the same characters as in Fig. 1.

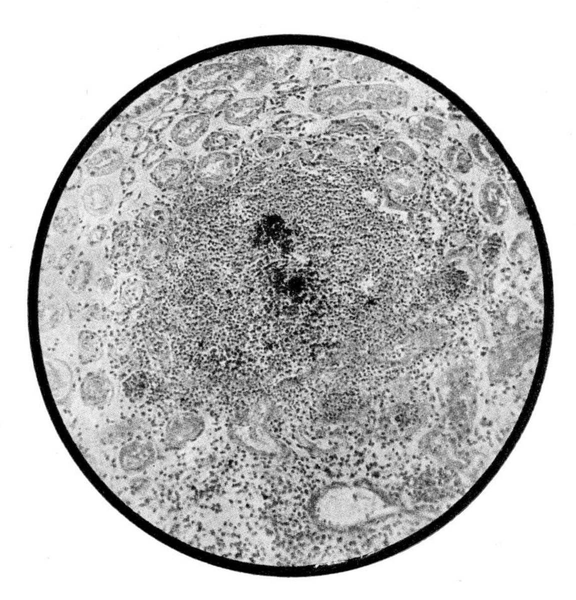

FIG. 3.

× **75.** *Gram's stain.*

Section of kidney from experimental animal showing **staphylococcal** abscess. Note masses of Gram-positive staphylococci, stained violet, in centre of abscess.

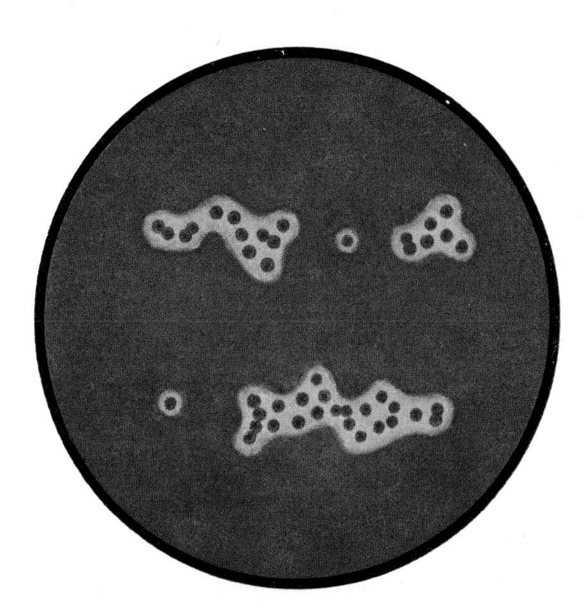

FIG. 4.

Colonies of **Staphylococcus aureus** on blood agar medium: 12 hours growth: actual size: looked at by transmitted light. Note the well marked hæmolysis and compare the large opaque colony with the smaller more translucent colony of Streptococcus pyogenes in Fig. 13.

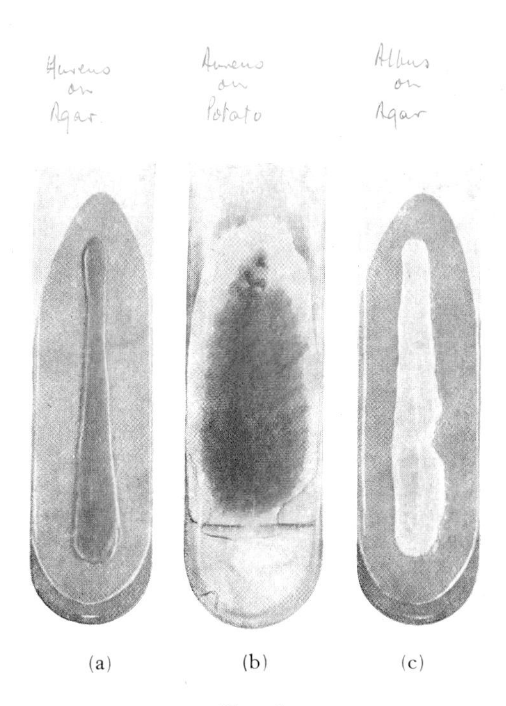

FIG. 5.

(a) Stroke culture of **Staphylococcus pyogenes aureus** on ordinary agar. Note smooth shining opaque golden-yellow growth like a streak of oil paint.

(b) Stroke culture of **Staphylococcus aureus** on potato. The bright yellow colour is characteristic.

(c) Stroke culture of **Staphylococcus pyogenes albus** on ordinary agar. Note the same characteristics as in (a) except that the growth is white.

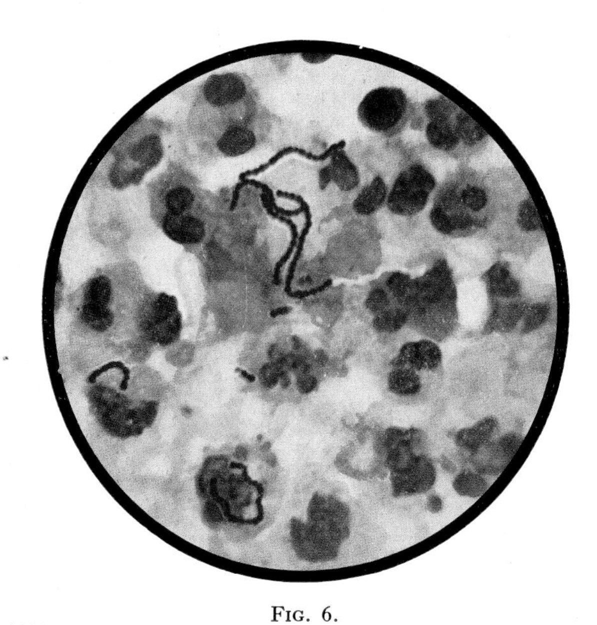

Fig. 6.

× **1000.** *Gram's stain.*

Film of pus from abscess showing **hæmolytic streptococcus ;** spherical Gram-positive coccus in chains of medium length.

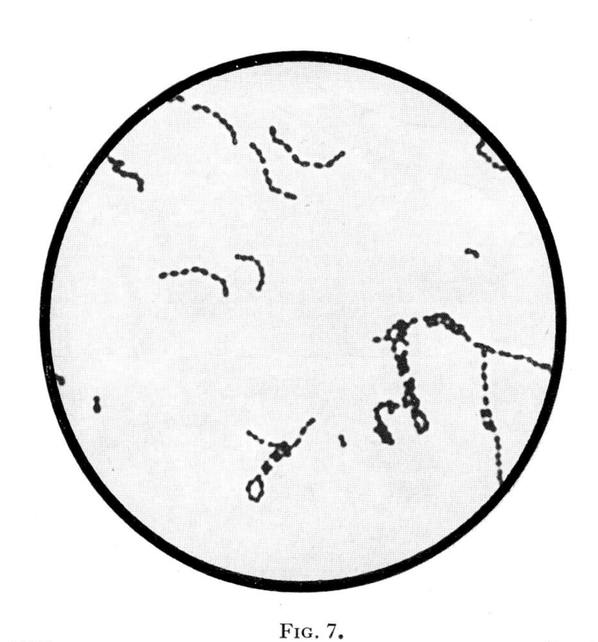

Fig. 7.

× **1000.** *Gram's stain.*

Film of culture of **hæmolytic streptococcus** in nutrient broth; a spherical and ovoid Gram-positive coccus in chains of medium length.

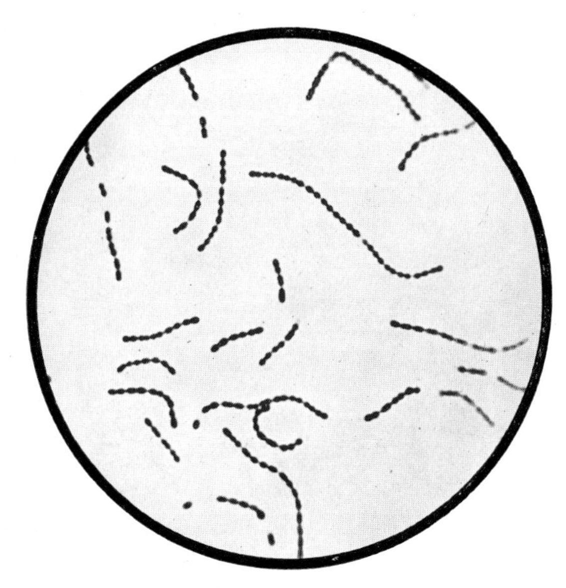

FIG. 8.

× **1000.** *Gram's stain.*

Film of culture of **Streptococcus viridans** in nutrient broth : a spherical and ovoid Gram-positive coccus in long chains.

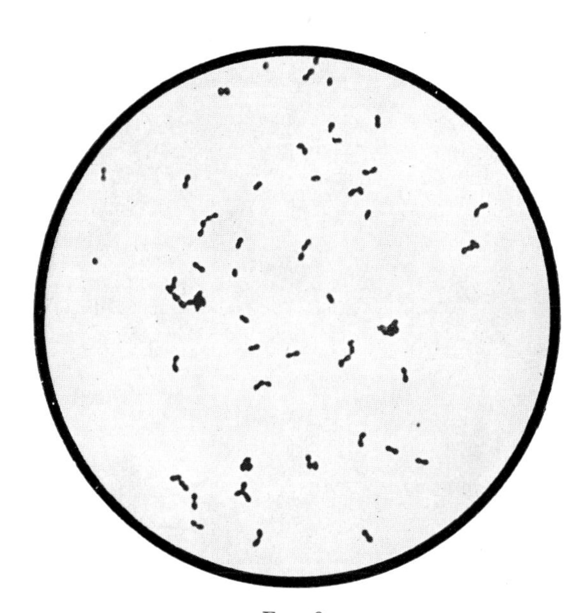

FIG. 9.

× **1000.** *Gram's stain.*

Film of culture of **Streptococcus fæcalis (enterococcus)** in nutrient broth showing a Gram-positive oval coccus in diplococcal formation and short chains.

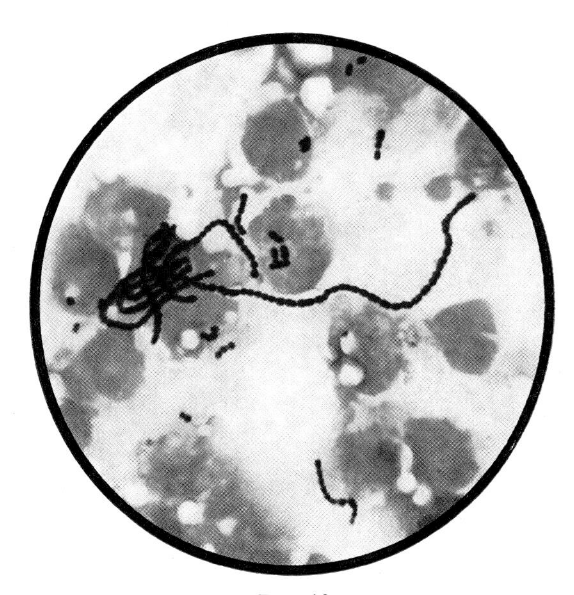

FIG. 10.

× **1000.** *Gram's stain.*

Smear from udder of cow suffering from mastitis showing **Streptococcus agalactiæ**—a spherical Gram-positive coccus in very long chains.

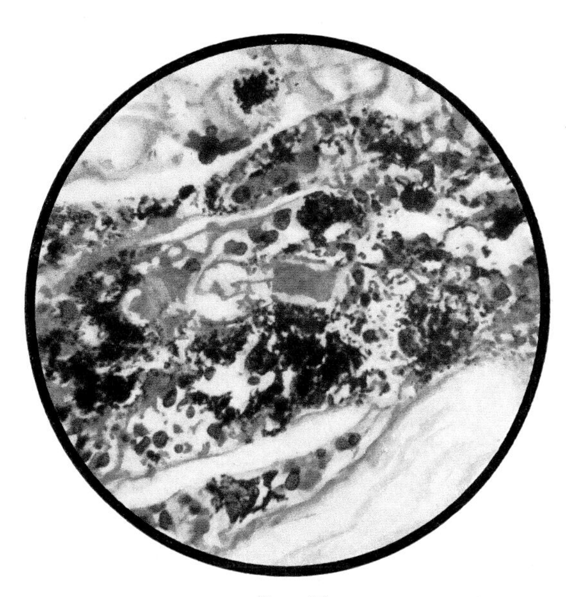

FIG. 11.

× **500.** *Gram's stain.*

Section of deltoid muscle from fatal case of Septic cellulitis showing numerous collections of **Streptococcus pyogenes** (stained violet) in the muscle. Note the separation of the muscle fibres by sero-purulent exudate.

α Haemolytic S. Viridans no or only v. little haemolysis.

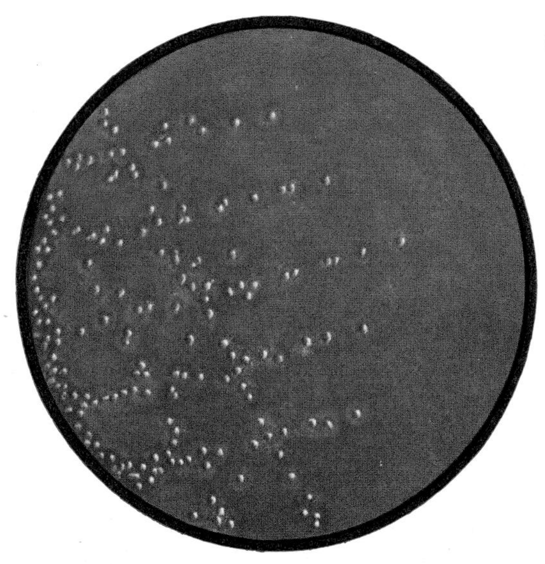

Green surround due to peroxidase formation and production of Methaemoglobin.

FIG. 12.

Colonies of **Streptococcus viridans** on blood agar medium: 18 hours growth: actual size: looked at by reflected light. Note characteristic green colouration of the medium under and around each colony.

cf Culture of Staph: Aureus.

β-haemolytic strep: (Def. haemolysis)

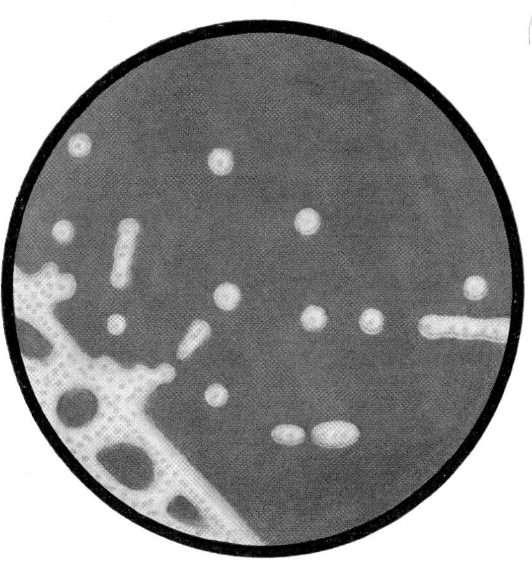

FIG. 13.

Colonies of **Streptococcus pyogenes** on blood agar medium: 18 hours growth: actual size: looked at by transmitted light. Note small round translucent grey colonies surrounded by a clear zone of hæmolysis. (cf., Fig. 4).

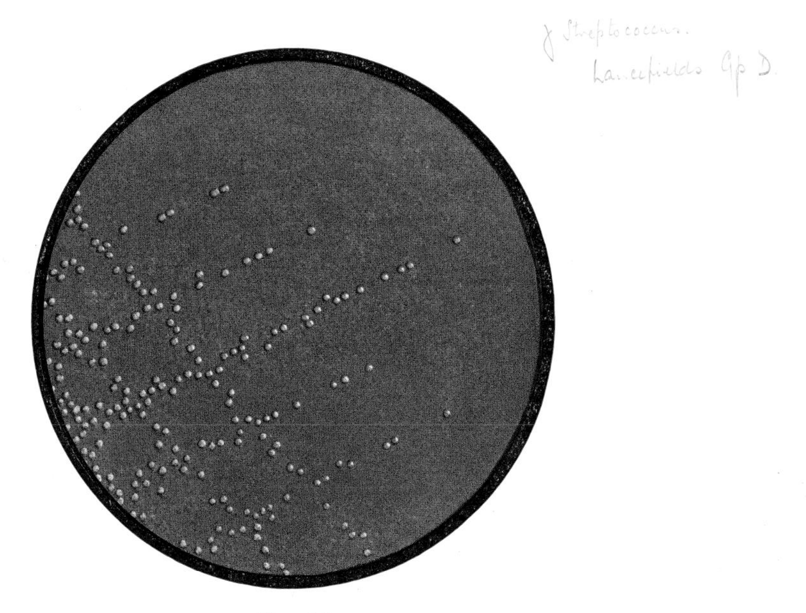

FIG. 14.

Colonies of **Streptococcus fæcalis (enterococcus)** on blood agar medium: 18 hours growth: actual size: looked at by reflected light. Note small round translucent colonies and absence of hæmolysis.

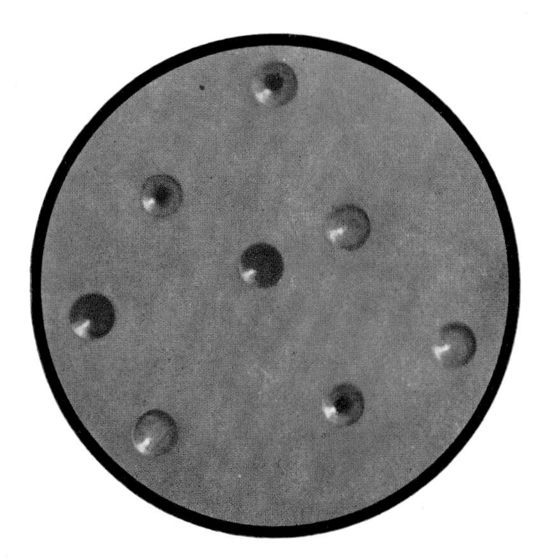

Fig. 15.

× 5.

Enlarged colonies of **Streptococcus fæcalis (enterococcus)** on MacConkey's medium : 18 hours growth : magnified 5 times : looked at by reflected light. Note three types of colony (i) pale pink, (ii) dark red and (iii) pale pink edge with dark red centre.

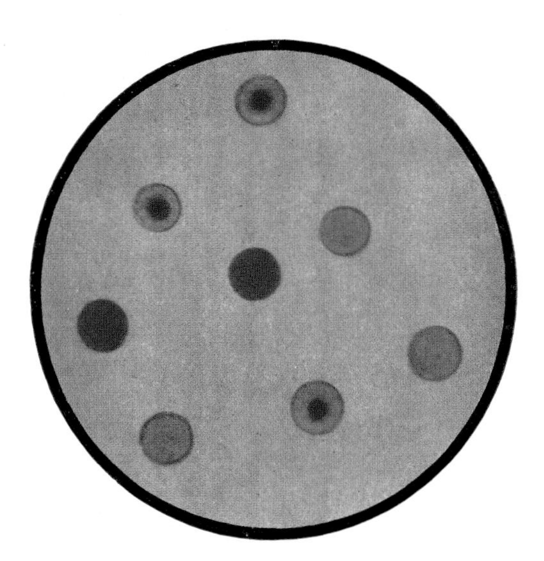

Fig. 16.

× 5.

The same colonies as in Fig. 15, looked at by transmitted light.

Fig. 17.

Stroke culture of **Streptococcus viridans** on boiled blood agar showing the characteristic yellowish green growth. A similar growth is also produced on this medium by **pneumococcus.**

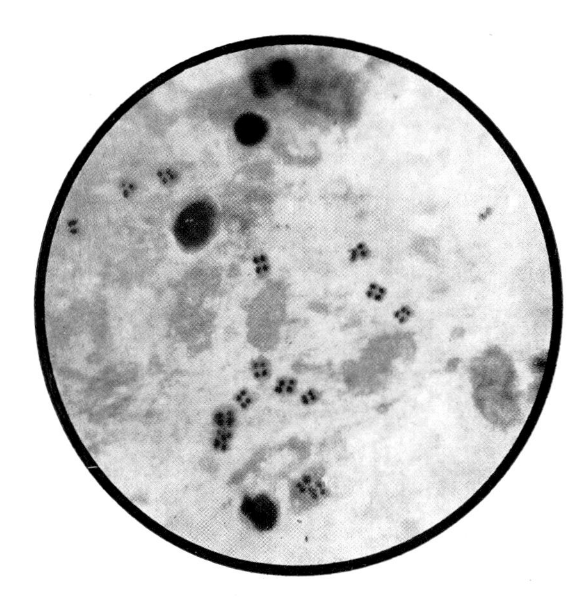

FIG. 18.

× **1000.** *Gram's stain.*

Film of pus showing **Micrococcus tetragenus** (**Gaffkya tetragena**) : Gram-positive spherical coccus arranged in groups of 4 (tetrads) enclosed in a capsule. Note that this organism is slightly smaller than the Staphylococcus. The staining of the capsule by the Gram counter-stain is unusual.

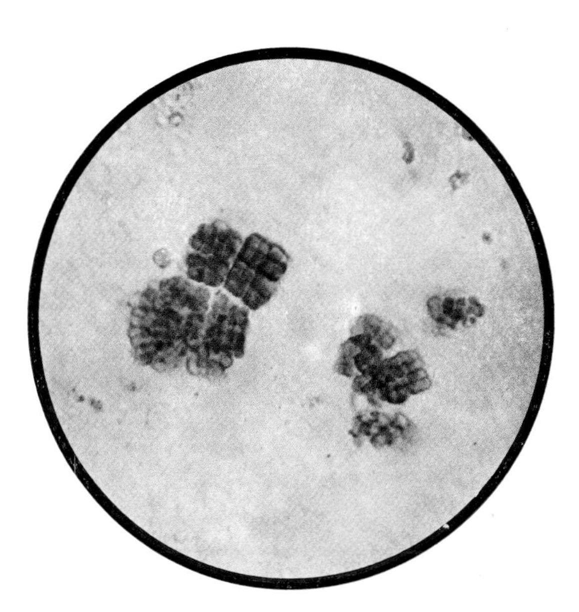

FIG. 19.

× **600.** *unstained.*

Stomach contents examined in unstained condition in normal saline showing **Sarcina** : a large coccus arranged in packets of eight or multiples of eight.

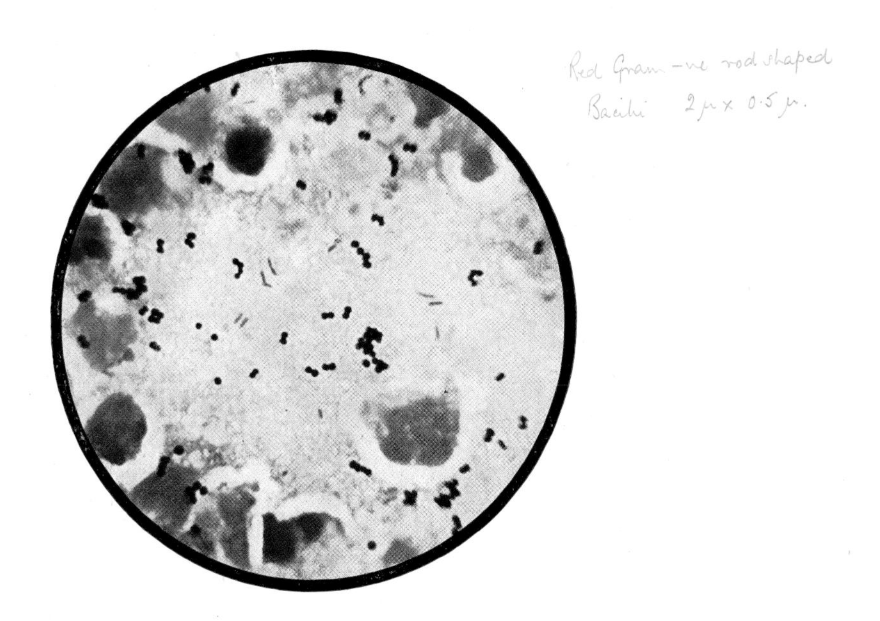

FIG. 20.

× **1000.** *Gram's stain.*

Film of pus from abscess showing **Bacillus pyocyaneus** (**Pseudomonas æruginosa**)—a medium sized Gram-negative bacillus and staphylococcus—single, in pairs and characteristic clusters.

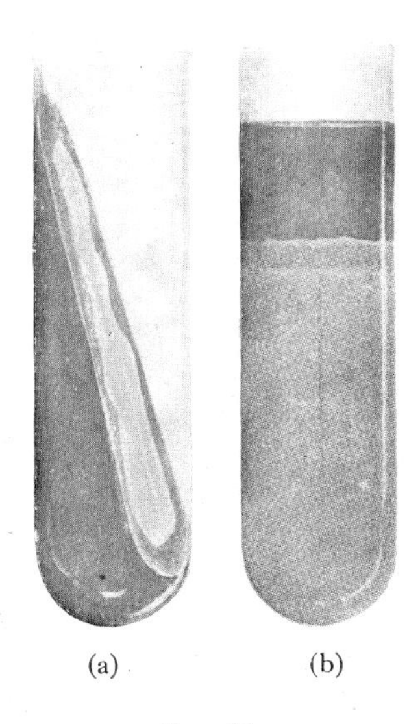

FIG. 21.

(a) Stroke culture of **B. pyocyaneus** on ordinary agar slope showing the characteristic grey-green translucent growth. The pigment (pyocyanin) produced by the growth has tinged the culture and diffused out into the medium so as to give it a blue-green fluorescent appearance.

(b) Stab culture of **B. pyocyaneus** in gelatin medium. Note the stratiform liquefaction with green-blue pigmentation of the liquefied area.

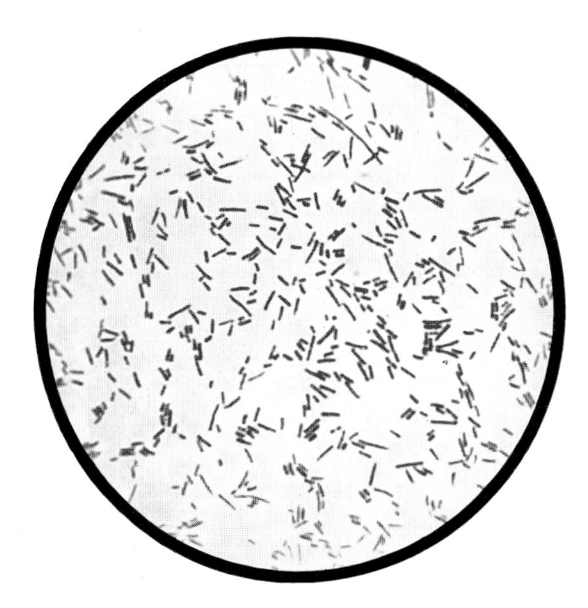

FIG. 22.

× **1000.** *Gram's stain.*

Film of culture of **Bacillus proteus** (**Proteus vulgaris**)—a straight Gram-negative bacillus with rounded ends; short, medium-sized and long filamentous forms are seen. This organism, when stained by Gram's stain, is morphologically indistinguishable from **B. pyocyaneus** and all the intestinal coliform organisms.

FIG. 23.

Culture of **B. proteus** on blood agar medium: 18 hours growth: actual size. Note the way in which the grey translucent growth has spread in waves over the medium: also commencing hæmolysis in the inoculation "well."

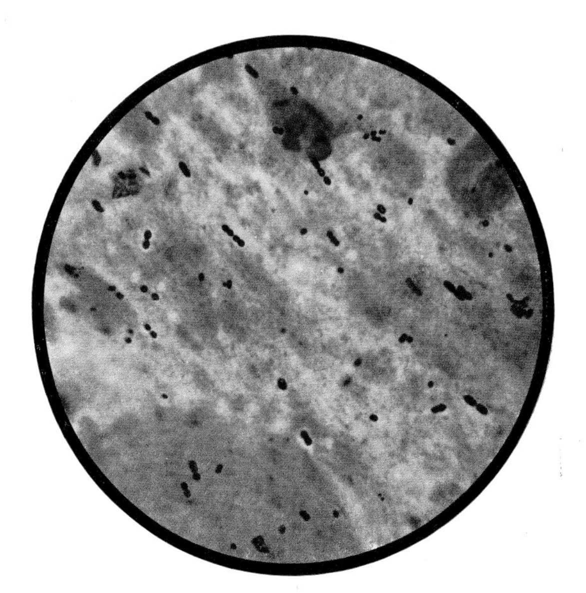

Fig. 24.

× **1000.** *Gram's stain.*

Film of sputum from case of Pneumonia showing the **Pneumococcus:** a Gram-positive lanceolate diplococcus with the long axis of the organisms in line.

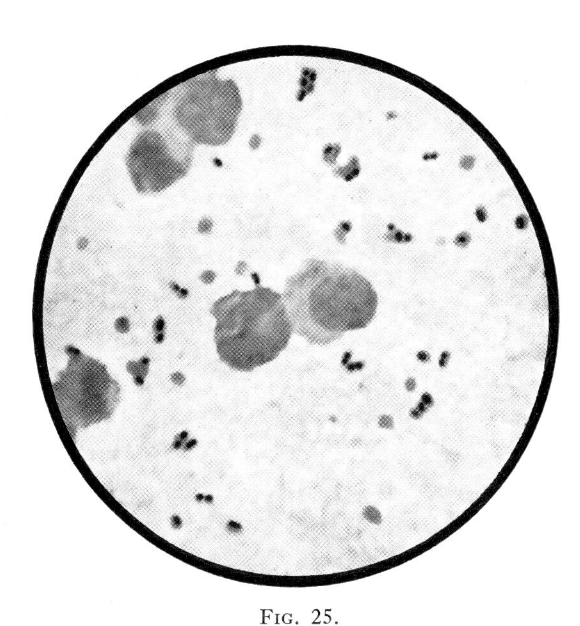

Fig. 25.

× **1000.** *Gram's stain.*

Film of sputum from case of Pneumonia showing **Pneumococcus:** a Gram-positive diplococcus enclosed in a capsule. Note that the staining of the capsule with the Gram counter-stain is unusual. (cf., Fig. 24).

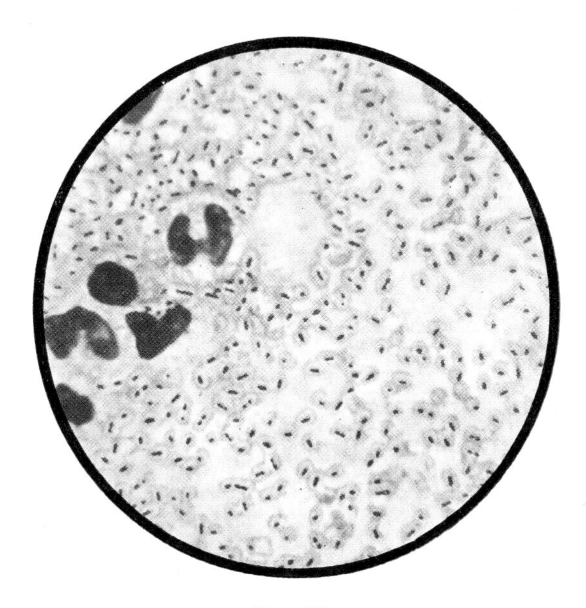

FIG. 26.

× **1000.** *Muir's capsule stain.*

Film of peritoneal exudate from mouse inoculated with **Pneumococcus,** stained red, and each pair of cocci surrounded by a capsule, stained blue.

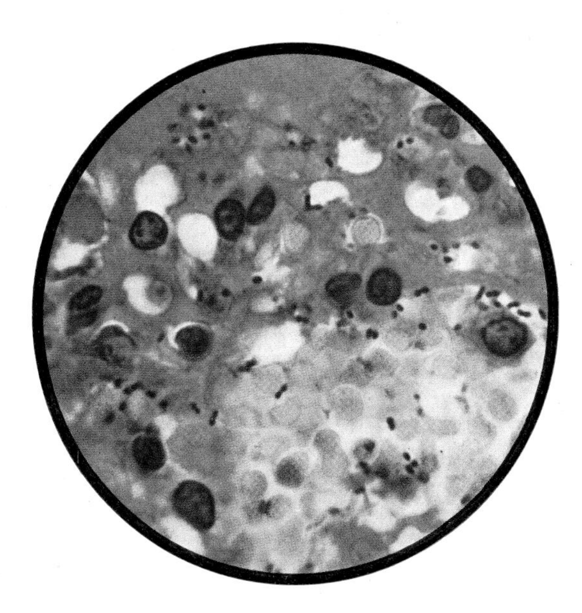

FIG. 27.

× **1000.** *Gram's stain.*

Section of lung from case of Pneumonia showing numerous **Pneumococci.** The capsule is not stained.

Greenish colony due to peroxidase liberation
and its action on Hb → Methaemoglobin (green)

Type III P. Mucosus very high mortality 45%
Occurrence 10% of Pneumonia Cases

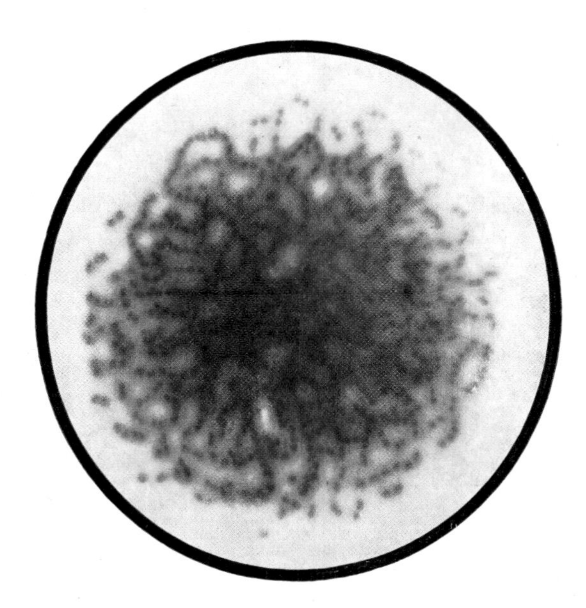

FIG. 28.

× **1000.** *Polychrome methylene blue stain.*

Impression colony of **Pneumococcus (type III)** : 12 hours growth on serum agar. Note capsulated diplococcus growing in chain formation.

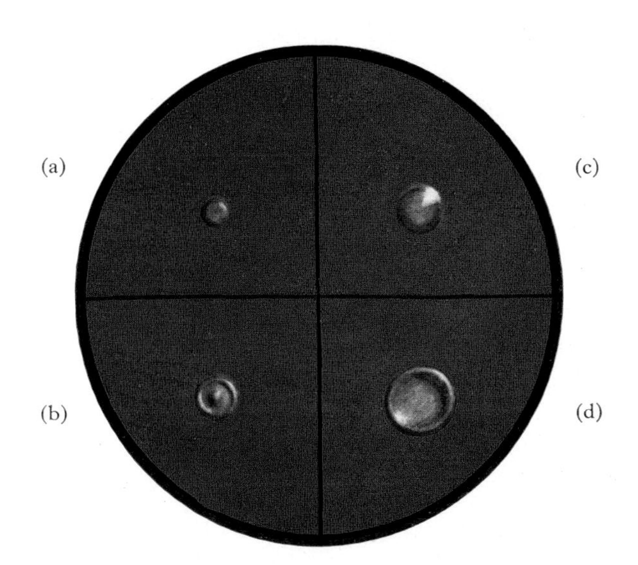

FIG. 29.

× **5.**

Isolated colonies of **Pneumococcus** on blood agar medium : magnified 5 times : looked at by reflected light. Note greenish colour of medium shining through the colonies.

(a). Type II. 24 hours growth.
(b). ,, 48 ,, ,,
(c). Type III. 24 ,, ,, " draughtsman " colony.
(d). ,, 48 ,, ,,

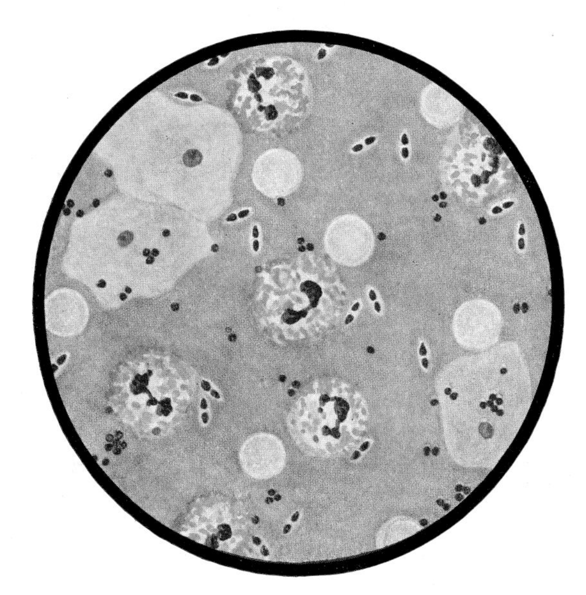

FIG. 30.

× **1000.**

Neufeld capsule-swelling test.

Fresh sputum from case of Pneumonia showing epithelial cells, erythrocytes, polymorph leucocytes, pneumococci and other cocci. The cell nuclei and organisms are stained by the methylene blue which has been added to the antiserum.

This pneumococcus is type I. after the addition of heterologous antiserum of different type showing a *negative* result with no swelling of the capsule.

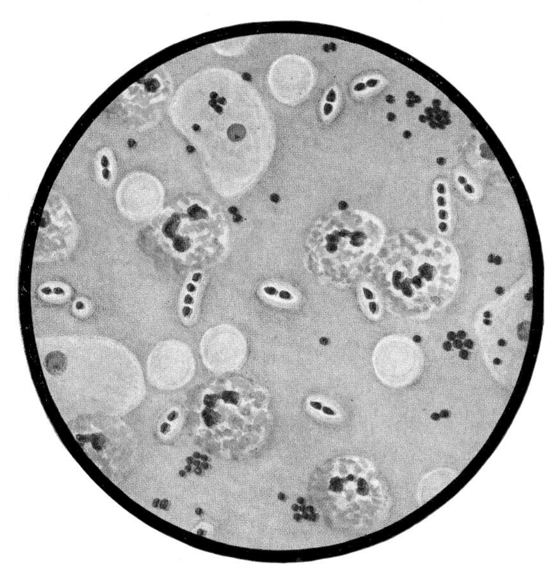

FIG. 31.

× **1000.**

Neufeld capsule-swelling test.

The same sputum as in Fig. 30 after addition of homologous (type I) antiserum showing a *positive* result with swelling of the capsule.

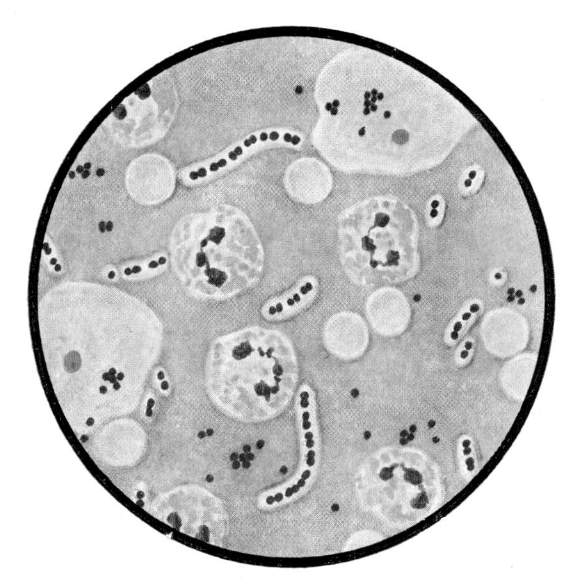

FIG. 32.

× **1000.**

Neufeld capsule-swelling test.

Fresh sputum from case of Pneumonia showing pneumococcus type III (pneumococcus mucosus) after the addition of heterologous antiserum of different type showing a *negative* result with no swelling of the capsule. Note the round shape of this type of pneumococcus and arrangement in chains.

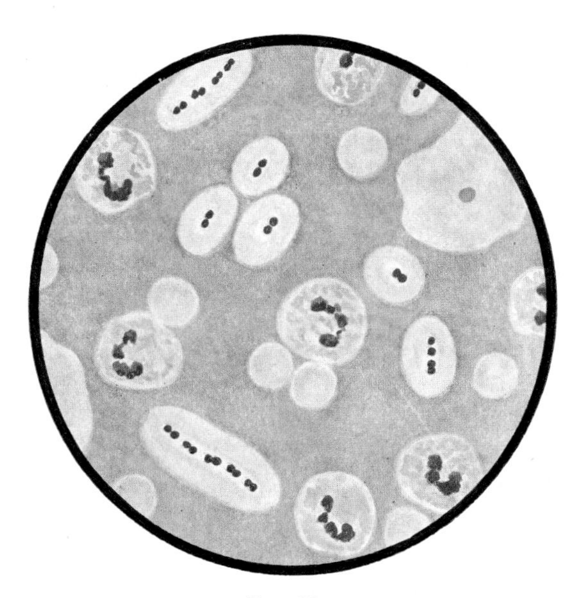

FIG. 33.

× **1000.**

Neufeld capsule-swelling test.

The same sputum as in Fig. 32 after addition of homologous (type III) antiserum showing a *positive* result with marked swelling of the capsule.

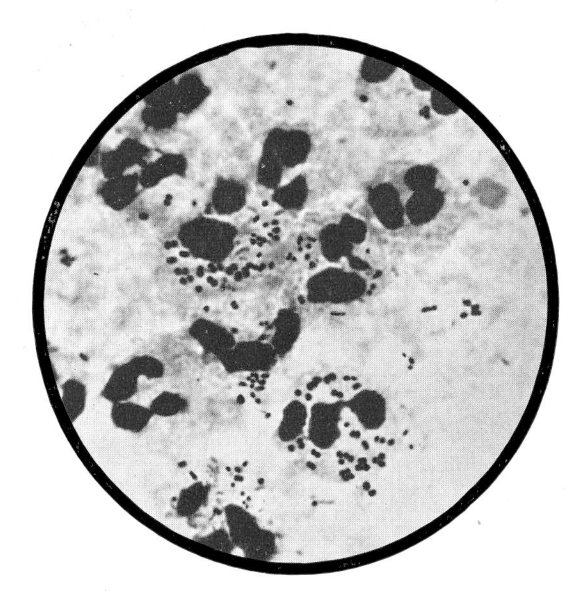

FIG. 34.

× **1000.** *Gram's stain.*

Film of pus from urethra showing **Gonococcus** (**Neisseria gonorrhœæ**) a Gram-negative oval diplococcus with apposed surfaces flattened or concave: the long axes of the cocci are parallel: nearly all are intracellular in polymorph leucocytes.

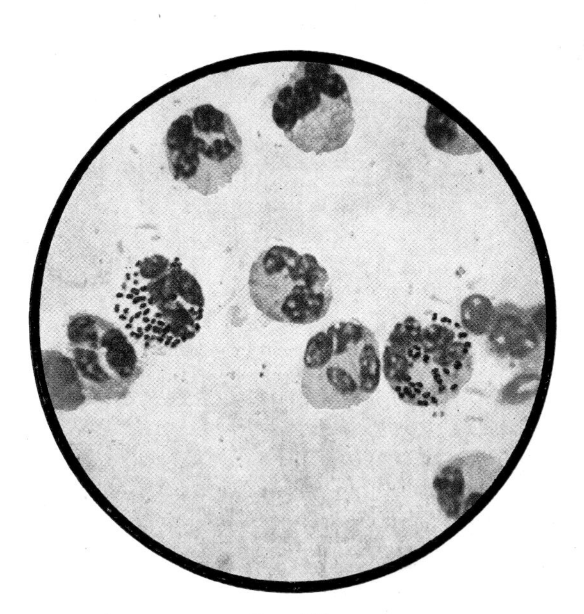

FIG. 35.

× **1000.** *Leishman's stain.*

Film of pus from urethra showing **Gonococcus.** Note the same characters as in Fig. 34.

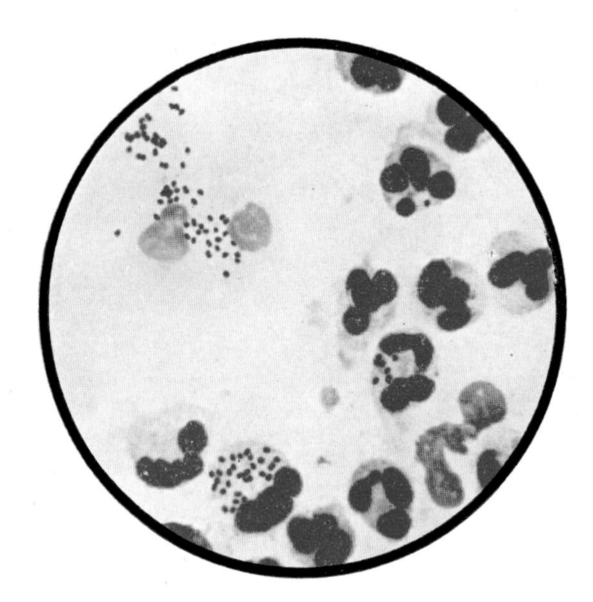

FIG. 36.

× **1000.** *Gram's stain.*

Film of purulent cerebro-spinal fluid from case of epidemic cerebro-spinal meningitis showing **Meningococcus** (**Neisseria intracellularis**). This organism is identical with the gonococcus in its morphological and staining characters and is also intracellular.

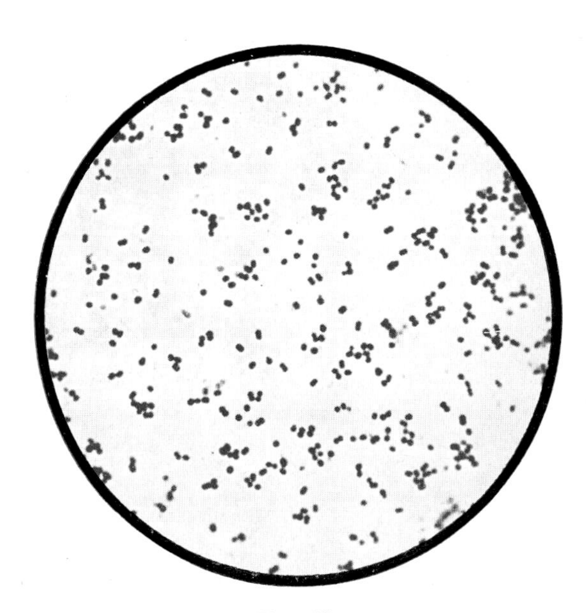

FIG. 37.

× **1000.** *Gram's stain.*

Film of culture of **Diplococcus catarrhalis** (**Neisseria catarrhalis**) on ordinary agar. Note the Gram-negative diplococci morphologically identical with the other Neisseria.

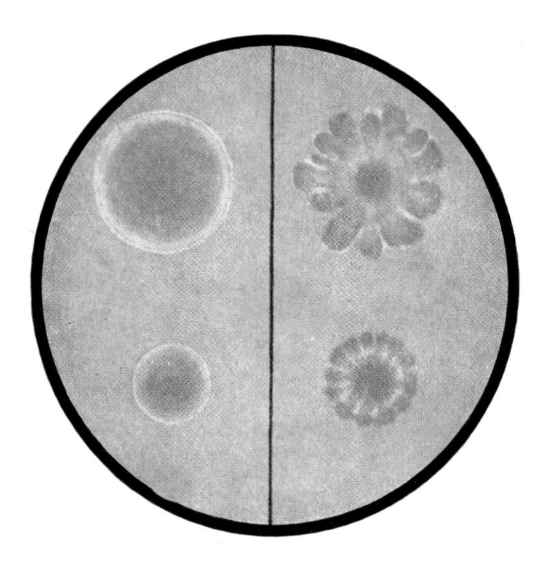

Fig. 38.

× **5.**

Enlarged colonies (× 5) on human serum agar of **Gonococcus** (right) and **Meningococcus** (left) looked at by transmitted light.

The lower colonies are 2 days growth, the upper ones 5 days. Note the semi-transparent greyish character of the growths. The gonococcus colony shows a scalloped edge whilst the meningococcus colony is circular with clear edge and more opaque centre.

DIPHTHERIA.

1. Gram +ve Corynebacterium
2. Chinese letter structure
3. Metachromatic staining. Volutin granules at poles.
4. Grows best on Serum media e.g.
   Loefflers & Blood Tellurite media
   Latter shows distinctive colonies.

5. Ferments Dextrose but not Saccharose.

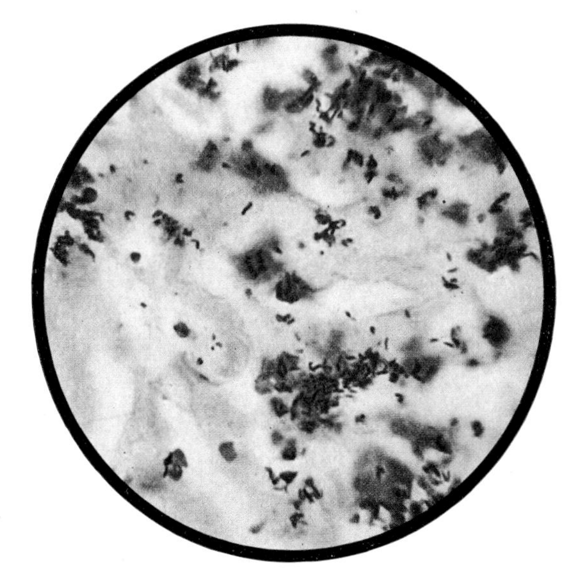

FIG. 39.

× **1000** *Gram's stain.*

Section of diphtheritic membrane showing Gram-positive **Bacillus diphtheriæ** (**Corynebacterium diphtheriæ**) in large numbers.

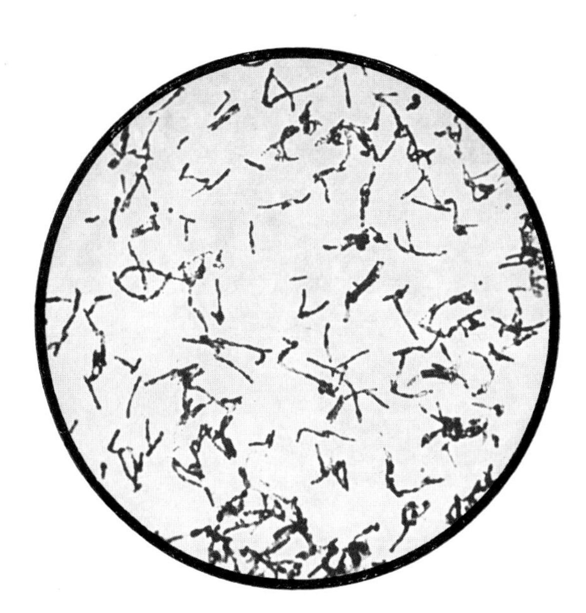

FIG. 40.

× **1000**. *Gram's stain.*

Film of culture of **B. diphtheriæ** on Lœffler's serum medium: slender, beaded, straight or curved bacillus. Note arrangement like Chinese letters.

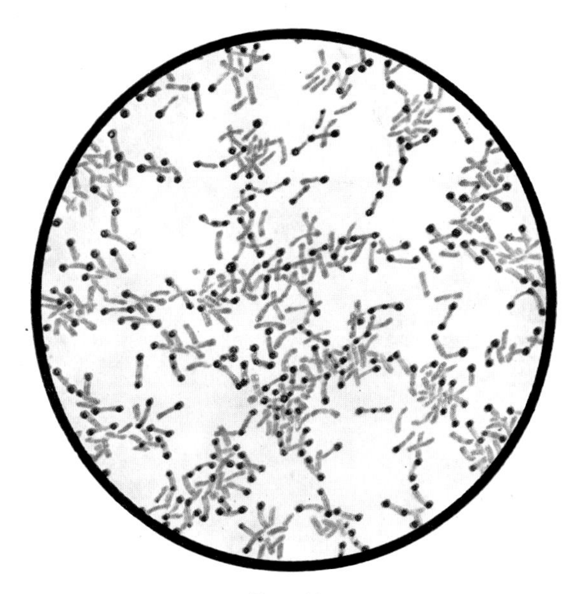

FIG. 41.

× **1000.** *Albert's stain.*

Film of culture of **B. diphtheriæ** (**gravis**) on Lœffler's serum medium showing a slender curved or straight bacillus stained green with metachromatic (Volutin) granules stained dark violet-black. Note the characteristic polar arrangement of the granules.

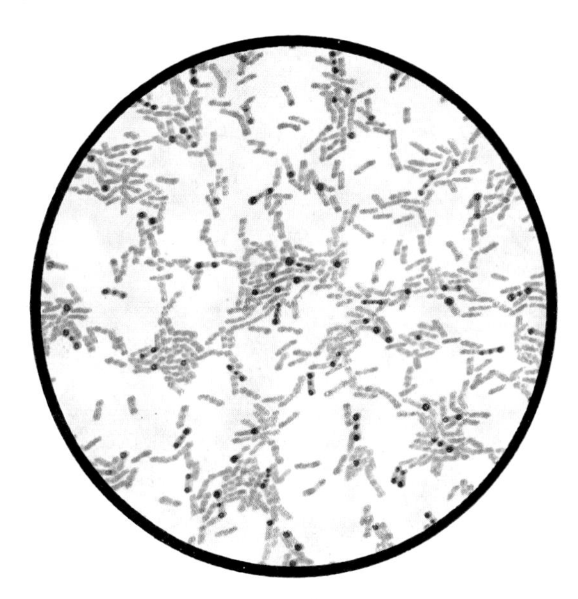

FIG. 42.

× **1000.** *Albert's stain.*

Film of culture of **diphtheroid** organism (*e.g.*, **B. xerosis**) on Lœffler's serum medium showing a resemblance to **B. diphtheriæ** but the organisms are not so slender, more barred and the metachromatic granules are less numerous and more variable in size.

FIG. 43.

× **1000.** *Albert's stain.*

Film of culture of **diphtheroid** organism (**B. hofmanni**) on Lœffler's serum medium showing a short bacillus with pointed ends and clear unstained bar in centre : no metachromatic granules are present. Note also the arrangement of the organisms side by side in rows.

(a) (b) (c)

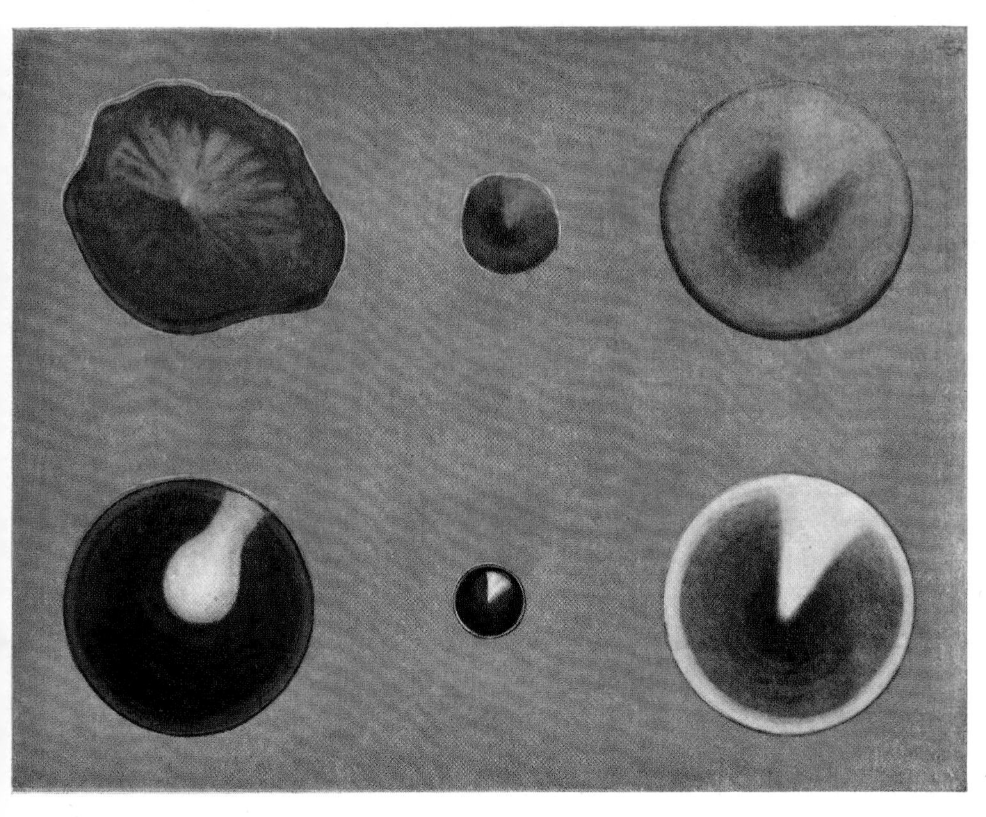

(d) (e) (f)

FIG. 44.

× **15.**

Enlarged (× 15) single colonies of **B. diphtheriæ, diphtheroids** and **streptococcus** on Hoyle's modification of McLeod's tellurite medium looked at by reflected artificial light after 48 hours growth.

(a) **B. diphtheriæ gravis:** Note matt surface: battleship-grey colour: raised centre with radiating sulci: irregular outline of edge.

(b) **B. diphtheriæ intermedius.** Note matt surface: battleship-grey colour, raised centre: no sulci: irregular outline of edge: only $\frac{1}{3}$ the size of the gravis colony.

(c) **B. diphtheriæ mitis.** Note matt surface: battleship-grey colour: raised centre: no sulci: perfectly circular outline of edge: large size, the same as gravis.

(d) **Diphtheroid** organism. Note very shiny surface, so much so that illuminating lamp reflected on it: jet-black colour: perfectly circular outline of edge.

(e) **Streptococcus** colony. Note shiny surface: brown colour: circular outline: very small size.

(f) **Diphtheroid** organism (*e.g.*, B. Hofmanni). Note shiny surface but less so than black **diphtheroid:** grey colour: perfectly circular outline of edge.

TUBERCLE

1. Non sporing, Non motile. rod shaped.
2. Acid & Alcohol fast.
3. "Antiformin" concentrates tubercles in scanty specimens.
   dissolves cells and other bacteria.
4. Culture on Dorset's egg medium or Lowenstein-Jensen medium. Glycerol-egg medium → Rough. Tough, buff, growth.

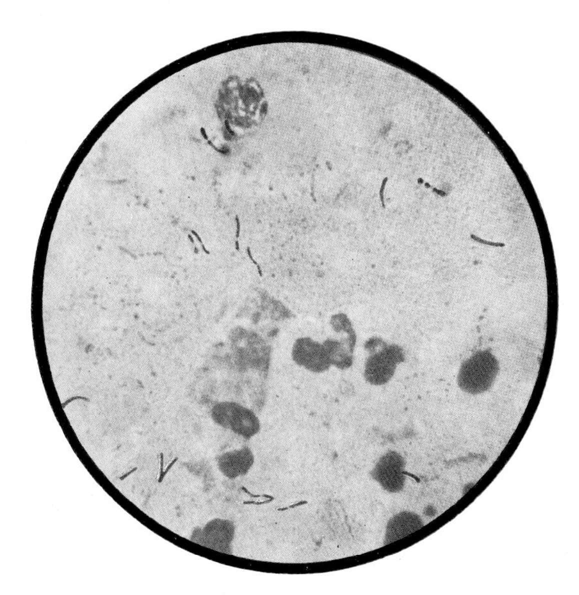

FIG. 45.

× **1000.** *Ziehl-Neelsen stain.*

Film of sputum showing the acid-fast **Bacillus tuberculosis (Mycobacterium tuberculosis)** stained red with carbol-fuchsin. The organism is a slender, straight or curved bacillus with rounded ends. Note the characteristic V arrangement of the bacilli.

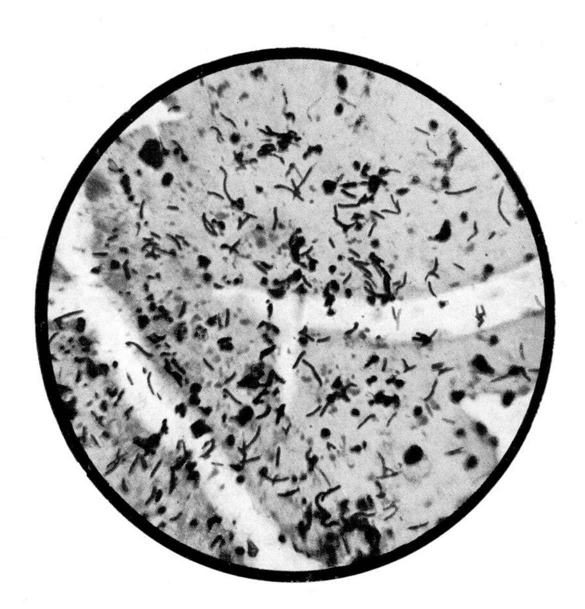

FIG. 46.

× **1000.** *Ziehl-Neelsen stain.*

Film of sputum treated with "antiformin," centrifuged and deposit stained with Z.-N. stain showing numerous **tubercle bacilli**. Note the granular masses of sediment and absence of cells (cf., Fig. 45).

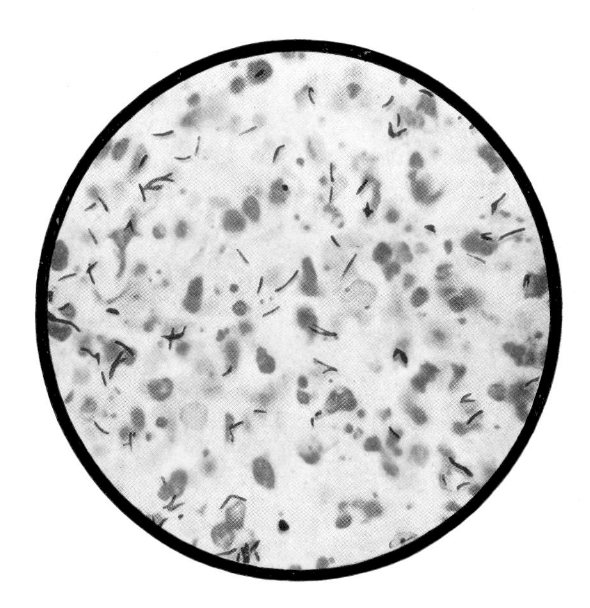

FIG. 47.

× **1000.** *Ziehl-Neelsen stain.*

Section of human lung showing numerous **tubercle bacilli.**

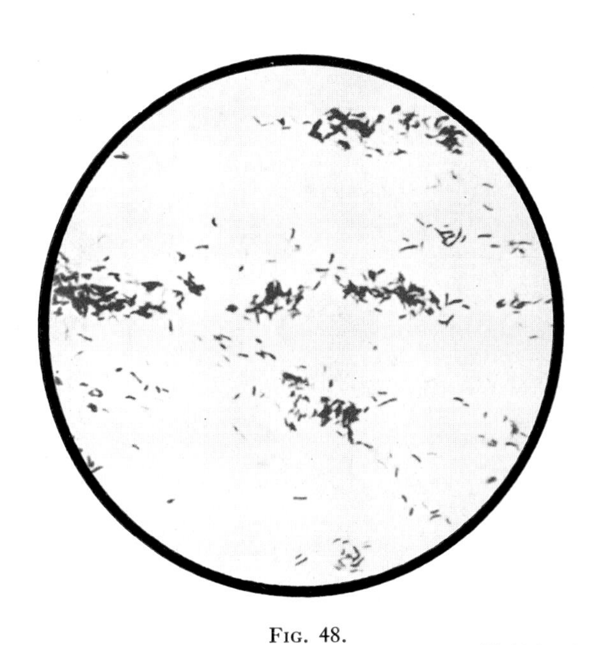

FIG. 48.

× **1000.** *Ziehl-Neelsen stain.*

Film of culture on egg medium of human type of **B. tuberculosis.** Note acid-fastness and characteristic clumps of organisms sticking together in bundles.

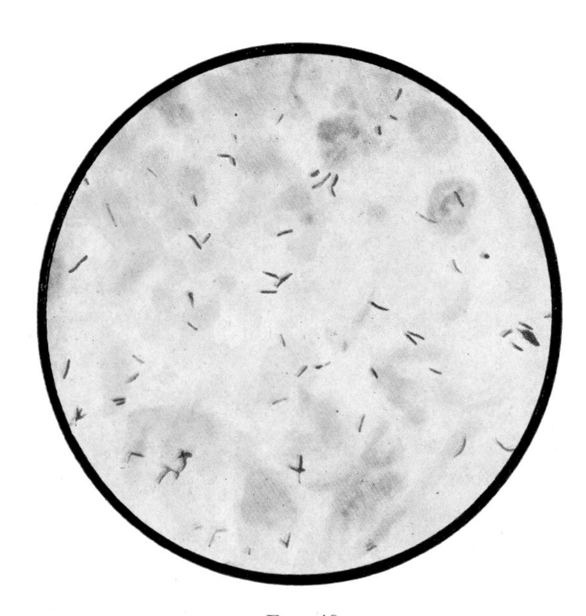

FIG. 49.

× **1000.** *Ziehl-Neelsen stain.*

Film of sediment of centrifuged milk from tuberculous cow showing numerous **Tubercle bacilli** of **bovine type** (cf., Figs. 45 and 47).

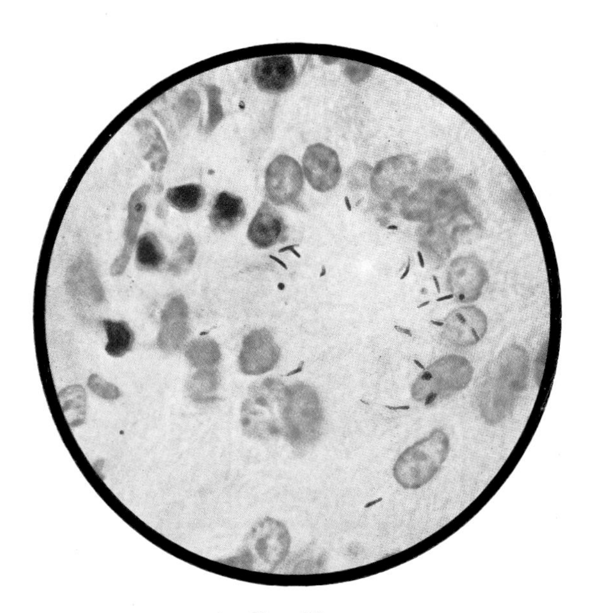

FIG. 50.

× **1000.** *Ziehl-Neelsen stain.*

Section of cow's udder showing **tubercle bacilli** of **bovine type** chiefly inside a giant cell.

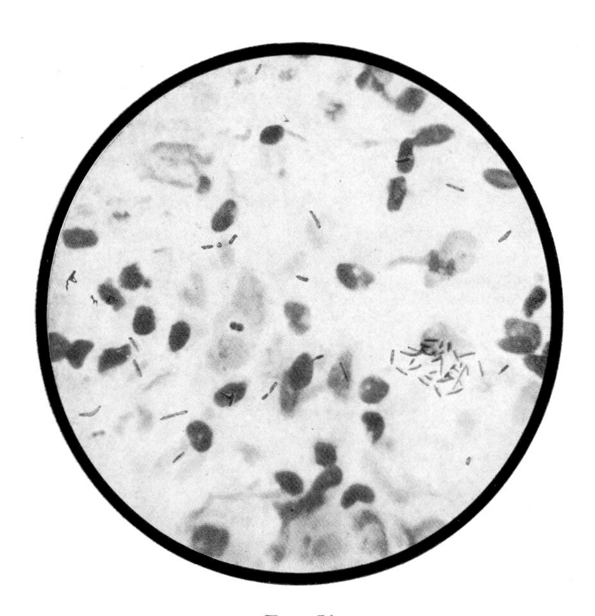

FIG. 51.

× **1000.** *Ziehl-Neelsen stain.*

Smear from fowl's lung showing **tubercle bacilli** of **avian type** (cf., Figs. 45 and 49).

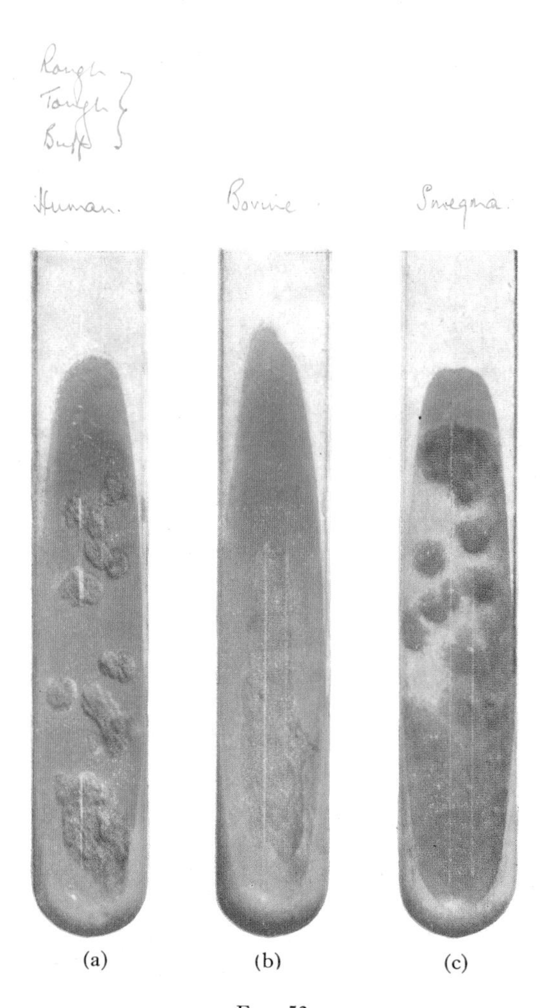

FIG. 52.

Cultures on *egg medium* coloured with *malachite green.*

(a) **Human tubercle bacillus**—showing characteristic mammillated buff-coloured tenacious growth.

(b) **Bovine tubercle bacillus** showing typical smoother paler less tenacious growth.

(c) **Smegma bacillus** showing yellow-red abundant growth.

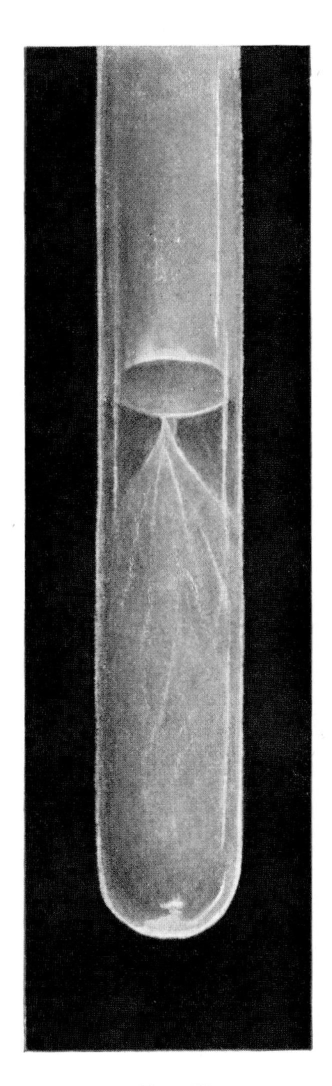

Fig. 53.
Cerebro-spinal fluid obtained by lumbar puncture from case of Tuberculous meningitis showing the "**spider-web**" **clot,** which is characteristic of the condition.

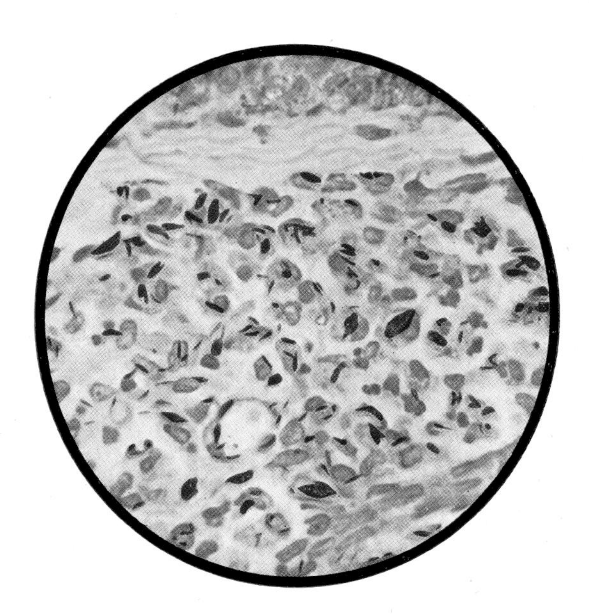

Fig. 54.

× **500.** *Ziehl-Neelsen stain.*

Section of skin from nodular **Leprosy** showing characteristic clumps of acid-fast leprosy bacilli chiefly inside cells.

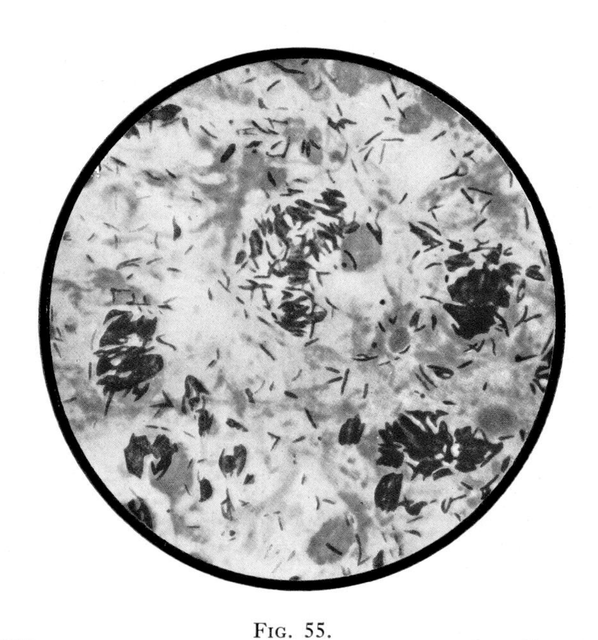

Fig. 55.

× **1000.** *Ziehl-Neelsen stain.*

Film of nasal secretion from case of **Leprosy,** showing very numerous acid-fast bacilli singly and lying parallel to each other in bundles.

FIG. 56.

× **1000.** *Gram's stain.*

Film of culture of **Bacillus mallei (Pfeifferella mallei)** the causative organism of Glanders—a short Gram-negative straight or slightly curved bacillus. Note also arrangement in chains and long filamentous forms.

Anthrax

1. Non motile, sporing, straight rod shaped bacillus
2. Chains. Spores are very resistant.
3. Stains Gram +ve. Spore unstained. Can use Mod: Z-N (½% Acid)
4. Aerobe & fac: anaerobe.
5. Agar culture → Inverted fir tree in Gelatin
   Goes into a crenated edge
   "Caput medusae"

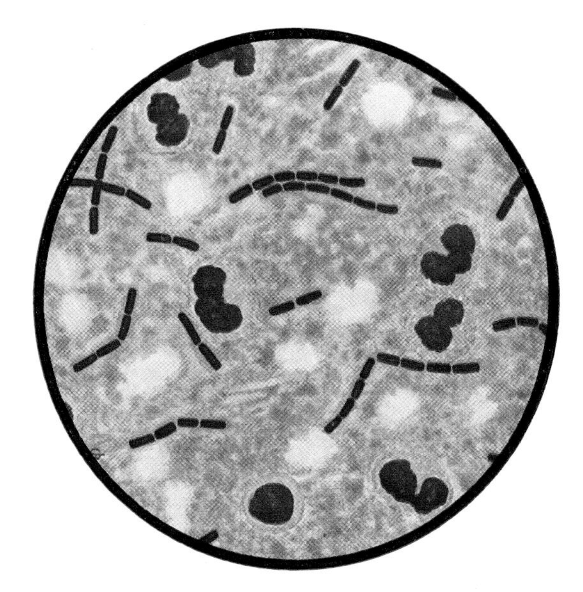

FIG. 57.

× **1000.** *Polychrome methylene blue stain.*

Film of blood from experimental animal showing the **McFadyean reaction.** Note large square-ended **Anthrax bacilli** and the characteristic bluish-red finely granular material. The clear areas represent the spaces from which red blood corpuscles have fallen out.

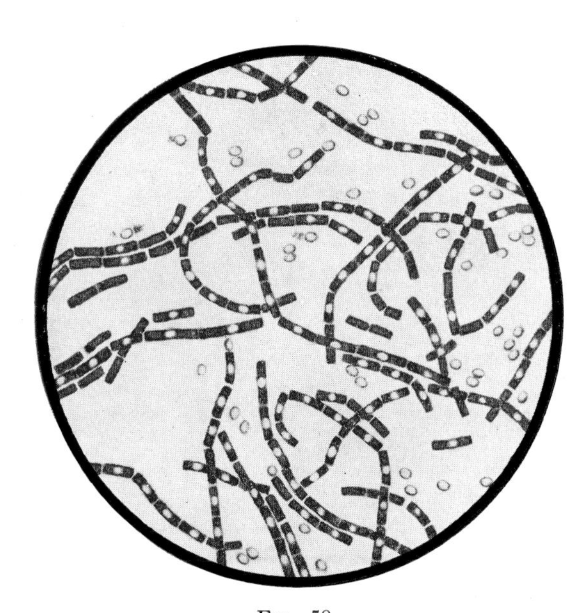

FIG. 58.

× **1000.** *Gram's stain.*

Film of culture of **Bacillus anthracis** on ordinary agar showing large square-ended Gram-positive bacillus, with central oval spore, in chain formation.

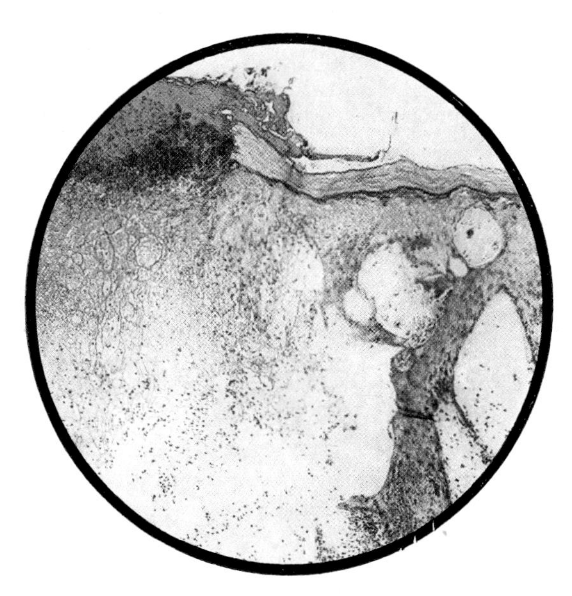

FIG. 59.

× **50.** *Hæmatoxylin-eosin-Gram-stain.*

Section of **malignant pustule** under low power showing masses of Gram-positive Anthrax bacilli stained deep violet. Note also serous exudate into cutis vera and bullæ in epithelial layers.

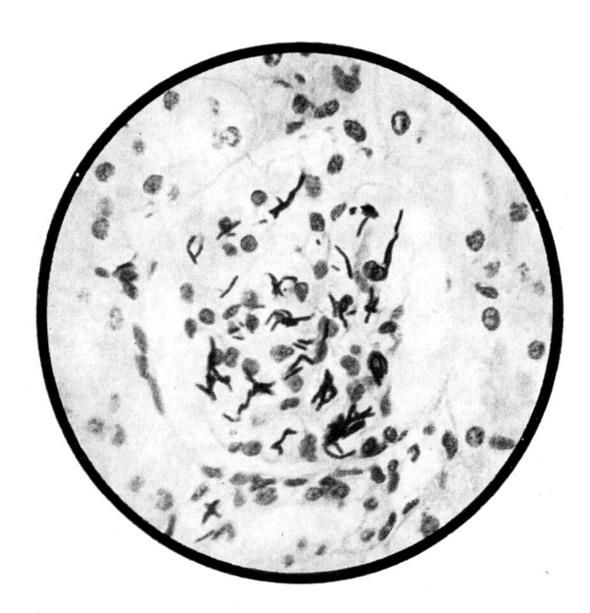

FIG. 60.

× **500.** *Gram's stain.*

Section of kidney of experimental animal under high power showing Gram-positive **Anthrax bacilli** in vessels of glomerulus. Note large size of the organism.

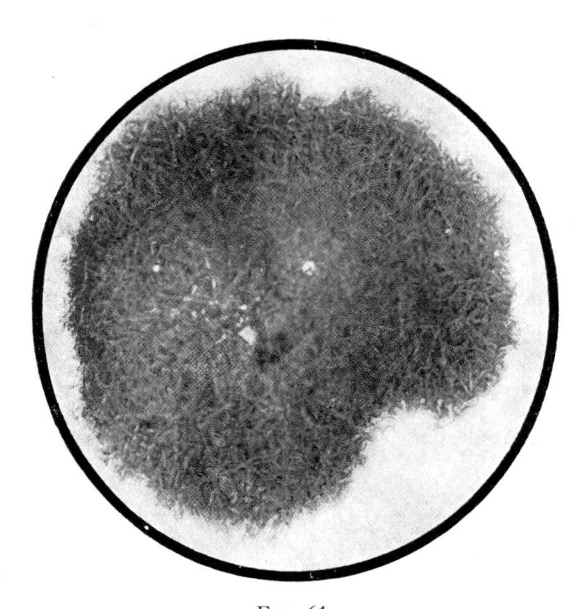

FIG. 61.

× **12.** *Methylene blue stain.*

Impression colony of **Anthrax bacillus** on ordinary agar medium. Note "hairy" edge of the colony.

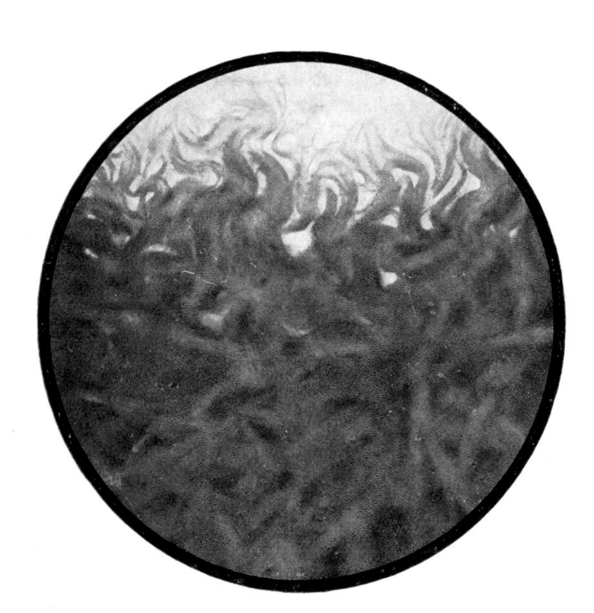

FIG. 62.

× **75.** *Methylene blue stain.*

Higher power view of edge of same colony of **Anthrax bacillus** as in Fig. 61. Note characteristic wavy hair-like growth.

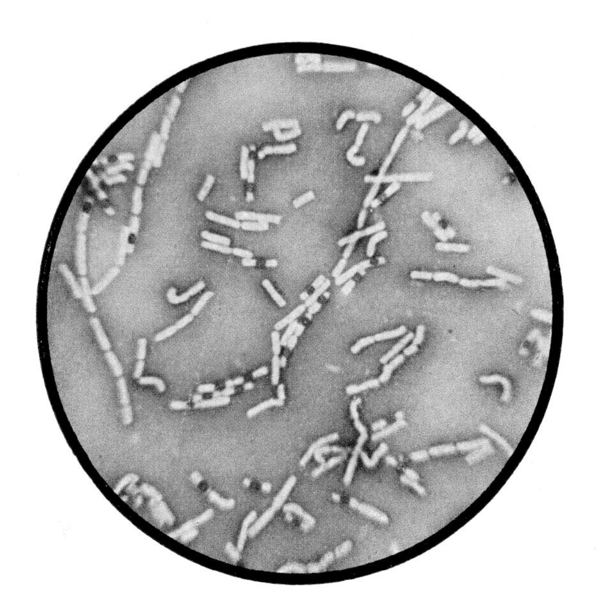

Fig. 63.

× **1000.** *Fleming's carbol-fuchsin nigrosin method.*

Film of culture of **Bacillus subtilis (hay bacillus)** showing oval central and excentric oval spores stained red in the unstained bacilli.

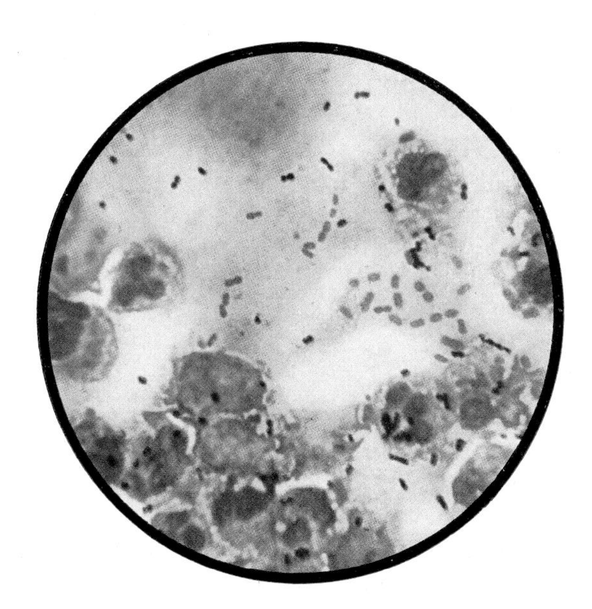

FIG. 64.

× **1000** *Gram's stain.*

Film of urine showing **Bacillus coli** and **Enterococcus.** Note short Gram-negative bacillus with rounded ends and oval Gram-positive coccus in pairs and short chains with a large number of pus cells.

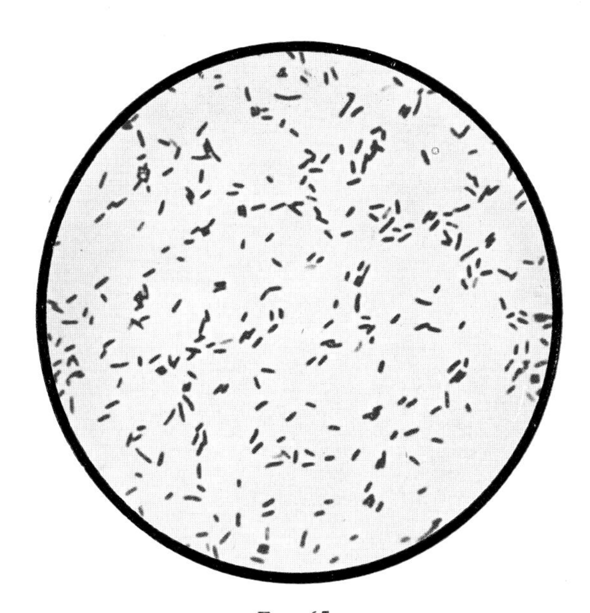

FIG. 65.

× **1000** *Gram's stain.*

Film of culture of **B. coli** in nutrient broth. Note Gram-negative straight bacillus varying considerably in length.

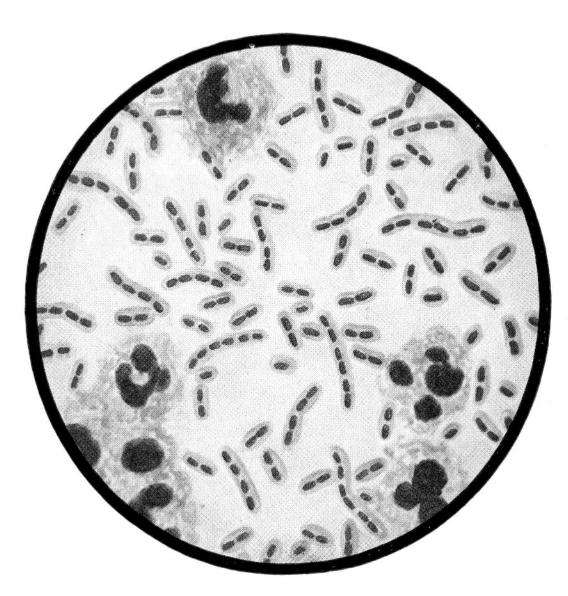

FIG. 66.

× **1000.** *Muir's capsule stain.*

Film of peritoneal exudate of mouse inoculated with **Pneumobacillus (Friedländer's bacillus)** a short bacillus, stained red, occurring singly, in pairs or short chains surrounded by a well-marked capsule stained blue.

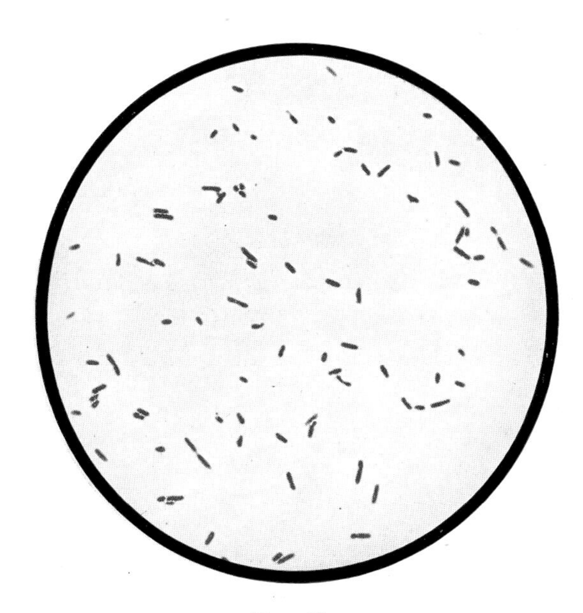

FIG. 67.

× **1000.** *Gram's stain.*

Film of culture of **Salmonella pullorum** the causative organism of "white diarrhœa" of chicks. Note Gram-negative coliform bacillus of variable length.

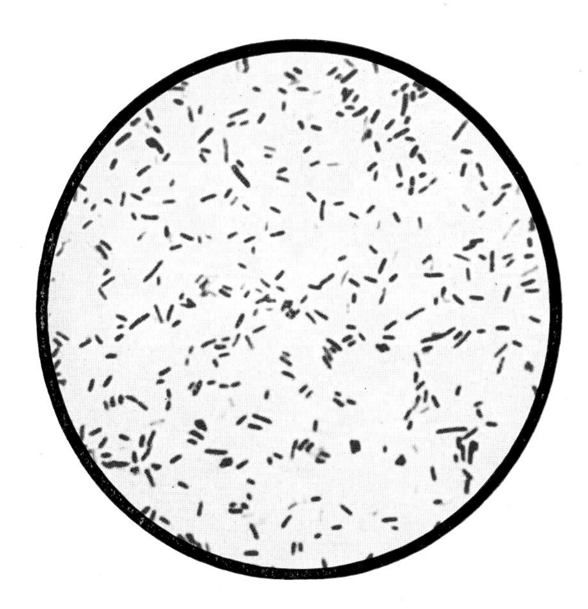

FIG. 68.

× **1000.** *Gram's stain.*

Film of culture of **Bacillus typhosus** in nutrient broth showing a medium-sized Gram-negative straight bacillus with rounded ends (coliform). Short and long forms are also seen. This organism is indistinguishable in its morphological and Gram-staining characters from all other coliform bacilli of the Coli, Paratyphoid, Dysentery and Salmonella groups.

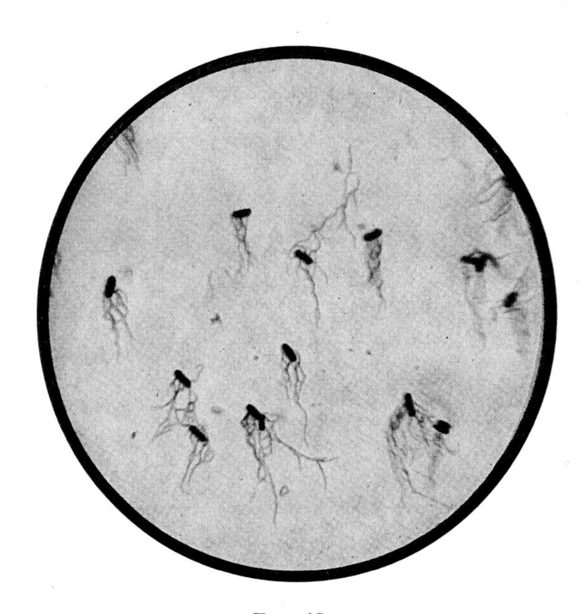

FIG. 69.

× **1000.** *Kirkpatrick's flagellar stain.*

Film of culture of **B. typhosus** stained to show the peritrichous flagella.

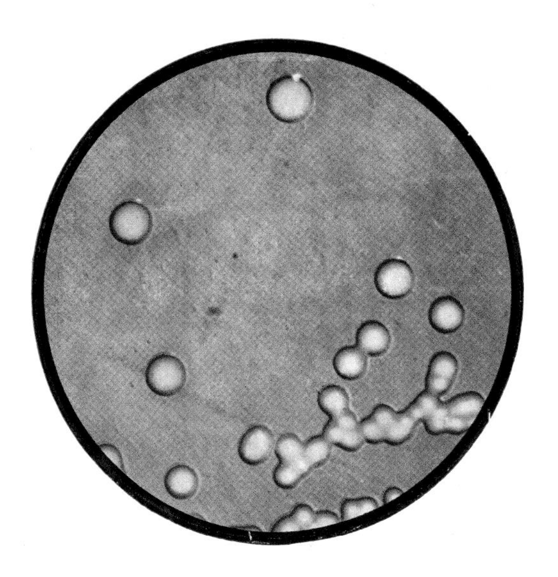

FIG. 70.

× 2.

Colonies of **Bacillus lactis ærogenes** (**Ærobacter ærogenes**) on MacConkey's medium : 18 hours growth : twice normal size. Note large raised, slimy, pink colonies.

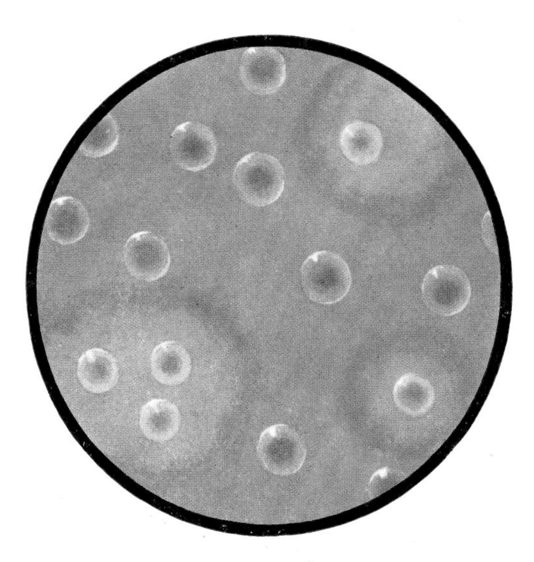

FIG. 71.

× $2\frac{1}{2}$.

Enlarged **pink** (**B. coli**) and **pale** (**B. paratyphosus B.**) colonies on MacConkey's medium: 18 hours growth: magnified two and a half times, looked at by reflected light. Note the " smooth " character of all the colonies and paleness of the medium round the pale colonies.

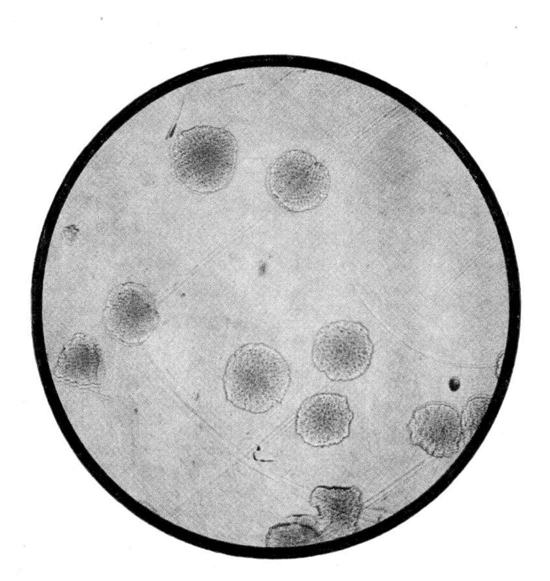

FIG. 72.

× $2\frac{1}{2}$.

Enlarged pale colonies of **B. paratyphosus B.** on MacConkey's medium: 18 hours growth: magnified two and a half times: looked at by transmitted light. Note the " rough " character of the colonies.

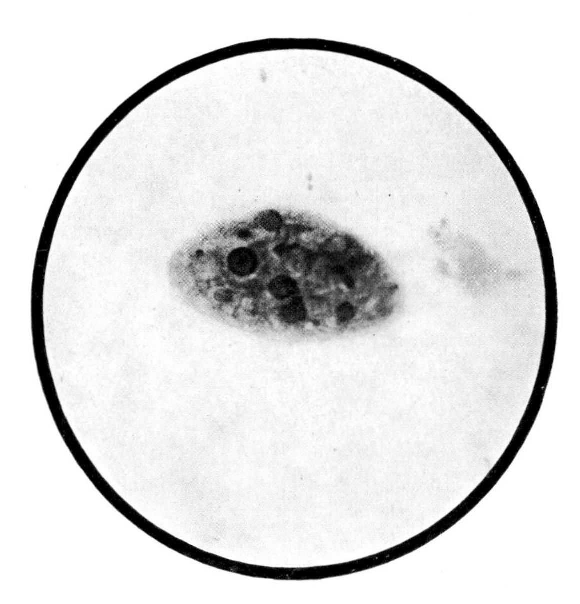

FIG. 73.

× **750.** *Hæmatoxylin and alcoholic eosin stain.*

Film of stool from case of amœbic dysentery showing the vegetative stage of **Entamœba histolytica.** Note the round nucleus with nucleolus, granular cytoplasm with clear zone at periphery and ingested red blood corpuscles.

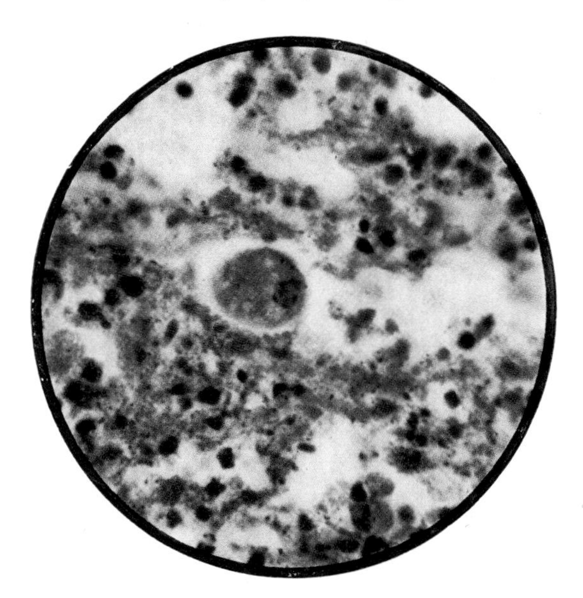

FIG. 74.

× **750.** *Iron-hæmatoxylin and eosin stain.*

Section of intestinal wall from case of amœbic dysentery showing the vegetative stage of **Entamœba histolytica.** The nucleus is stained black, the cytoplasm is finely granular except at the periphery and the characteristic ingested red blood corpuscles are also seen. Note that although the magnification is the same as in Fig. 73, the amœba is much smaller owing to shrinkage in fixation and preparation for section.

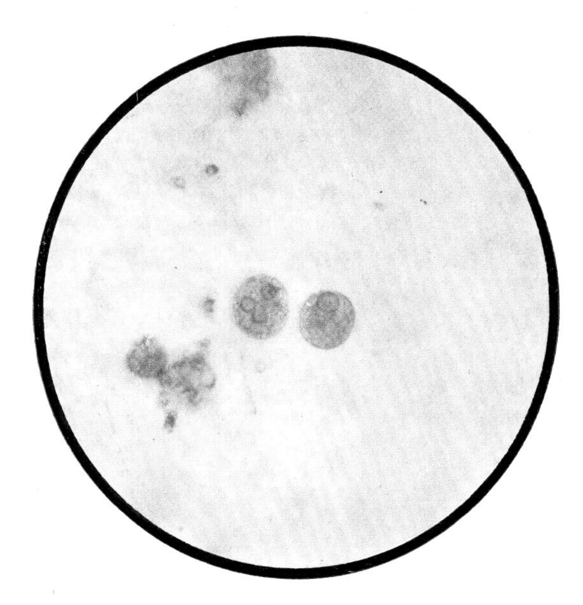

FIG. 75.

× **750.**

Film of stool from case of amœbic dysentery. Wet preparation with addition of 0.5% eosin solution showing the cystic stage of **Entamœba histolytica.** Note the sharp outline of both amœbæ. In one four small nuclei are visible, in the other the nuclei are all out of focus.

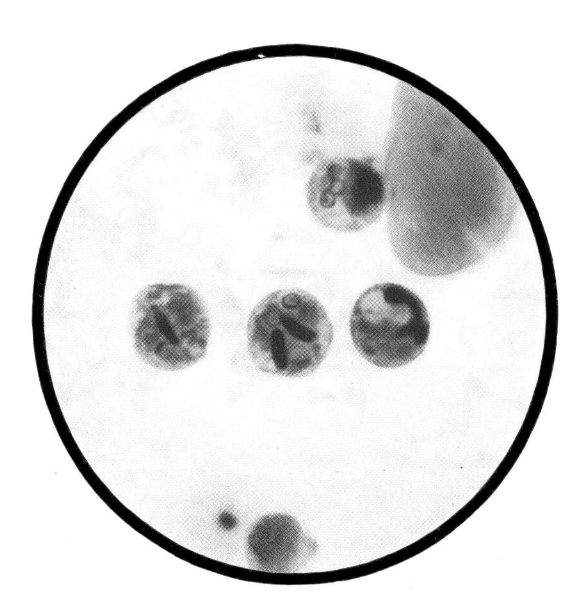

FIG. 76.

× **750.** *Hæmatoxylin and alcoholic eosin stain.*

Film of stool from case of amœbic dysentery showing the cystic stage of **Entamœba histolytica.** Note small number of nuclei (two or four) and deeply stained chromatoid bodies.

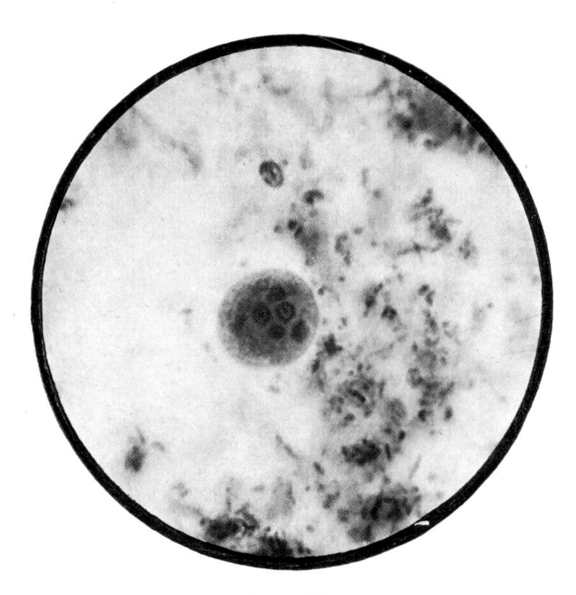

FIG. 77.

× **750.** *Hæmatoxylin and alcoholic eosin stain.*
Film of stool of normal individual showing the cystic stage of **Entamœba coli.** Note that there are more than four nuclei and no chromatoid bodies.

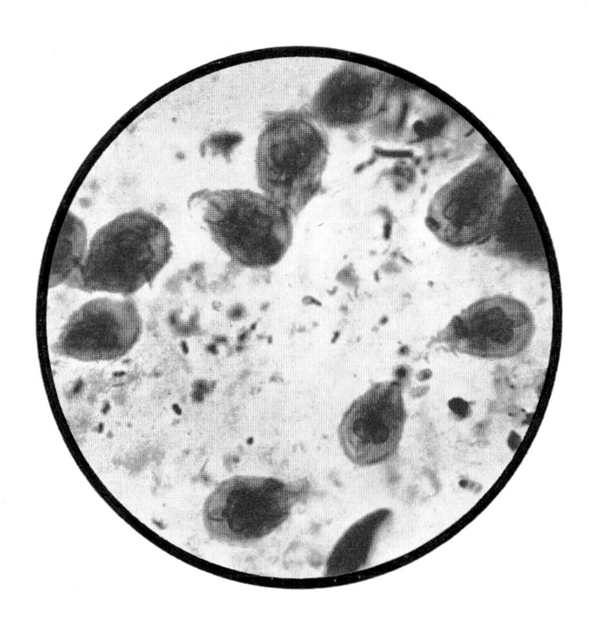

FIG. 78.

× **1000.** *Basic fuchsin stain.*
Film of fæces showing **Giardia (Lamblia) intestinalis.** Note pyriform shape with central axostyles on each side of which is a sucking disc. The flagella are not well seen.

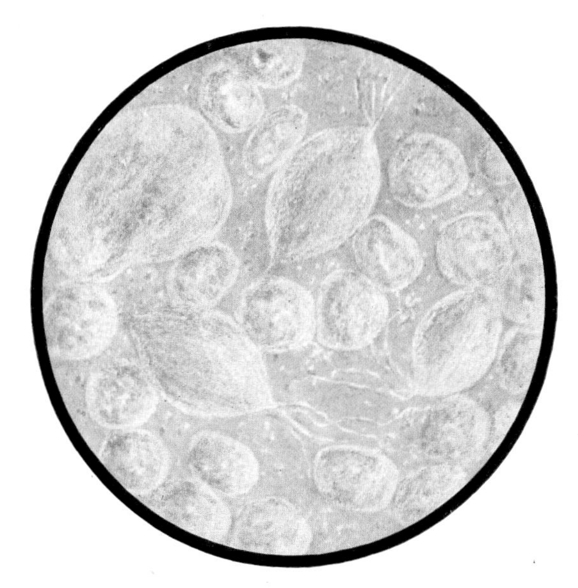

FIG. 79.

× **400.**

Fresh pus, in equal parts of normal saline, from a case of Vaginitis showing **Trichomonas vaginalis,** pus and epithelial cells : examined with oblique illumination by lowering the substage condenser.

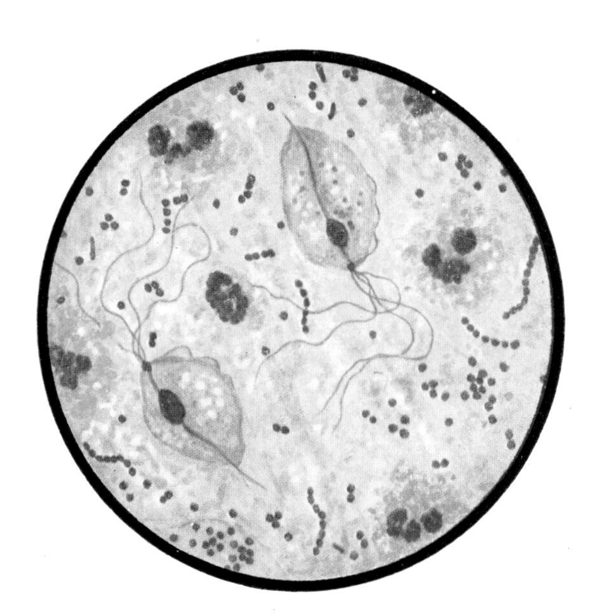

FIG. 80.

× **1000.** *Leishman's stain.*

Film from mouth showing **Trichomonas buccalis,** Streptococcus viridans, Staphylococcus and pus cells. Note axostyle running down the centre of the trichomonas, large trophonucleus and small kinetonucleus (blepharoplast) from which the four flagella emerge, undulating membrane and finely granular cytoplasm with vacuoles.

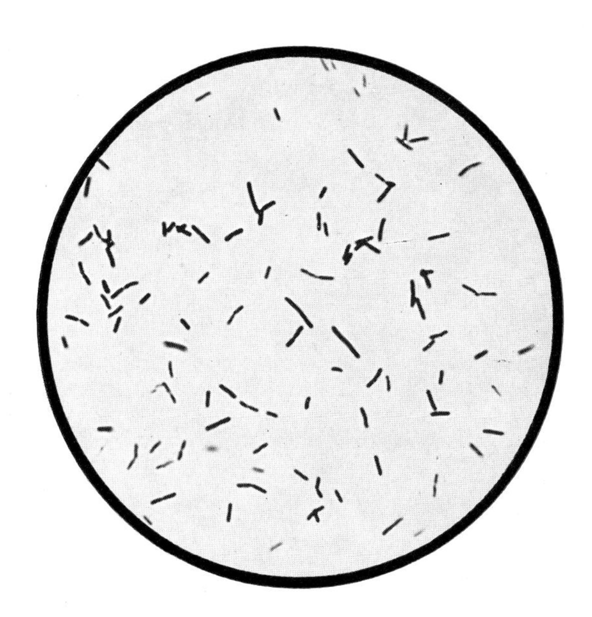

FIG. 81.

× **1000** *Gram's stain.*

Film of culture of **Lactobacillus acidophilus** in milk. Note straight, Gram-positive, relatively thin bacillus, single, in pairs and varying considerably in length.

CHOLERA.

1. Comma shaped, flagellate. No spores.
2. Gram -ve.
3. Alkaline media e.g. DIEUDONNÉ. Acid is inhibitory.
4. Aerobe.
5. Performs Cholera red reaction due to Indole prodn. & formn. of Nitroso-indole.

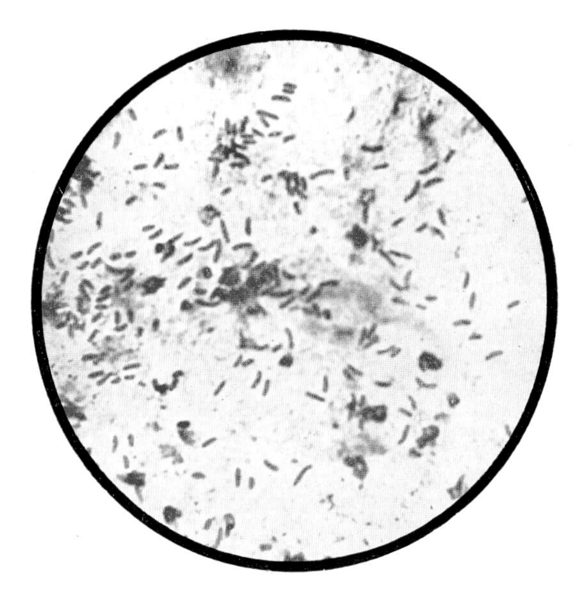

FIG. 82.

× **1000.** *Gram's stain.*

Film of stool from case of Cholera showing **Vibrio choleræ,** a Gram-negative curved (comma-shaped) rod. Straight Gram-negative coliform bacilli are also seen together with debris of desquamated cells of the intestinal mucosa.

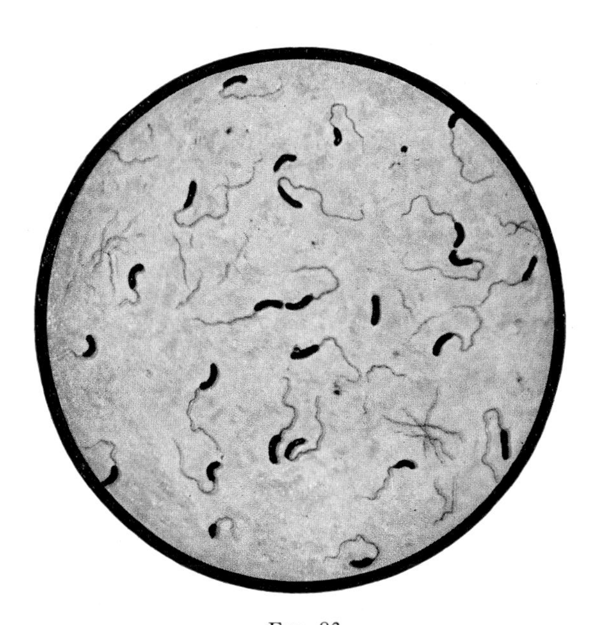

FIG. 83.

× **1000.** *Kirkpatrick's stain.*

Film of culture of **Vibrio choleræ** showing its terminal flagellum. Note that some flagella have become detached from the organisms.

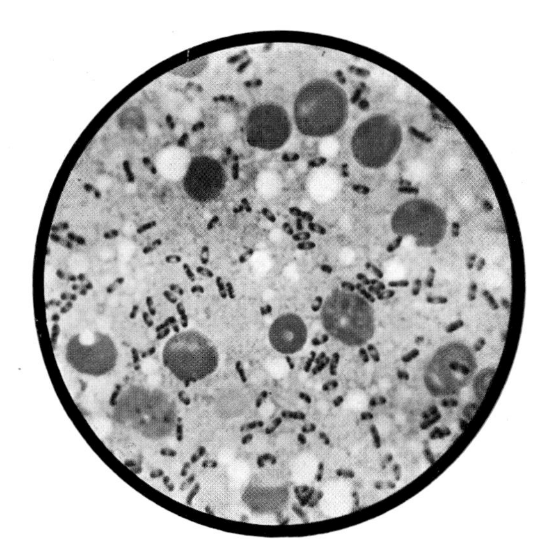

FIG. 84.

× **1000.** *Leishman's stain.*

Smear from human Bubo from case of Plague showing **Pasteurella pestis**—very numerous oval and barrel-shaped organisms showing characteristic bipolar staining.

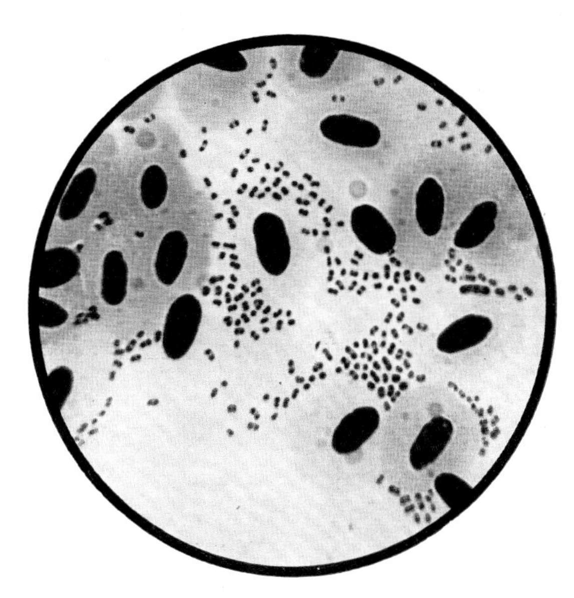

FIG. 85.

× **1000.** *Leishman's stain.*

Film of pigeon's blood showing **Pasteurella aviseptica,** the causative organism of fowl cholera and hæmorrhagic septicæmia of birds. It has the same morphological and staining characters as P. pestis. Note the oval nucleated red blood corpuscles of the bird.

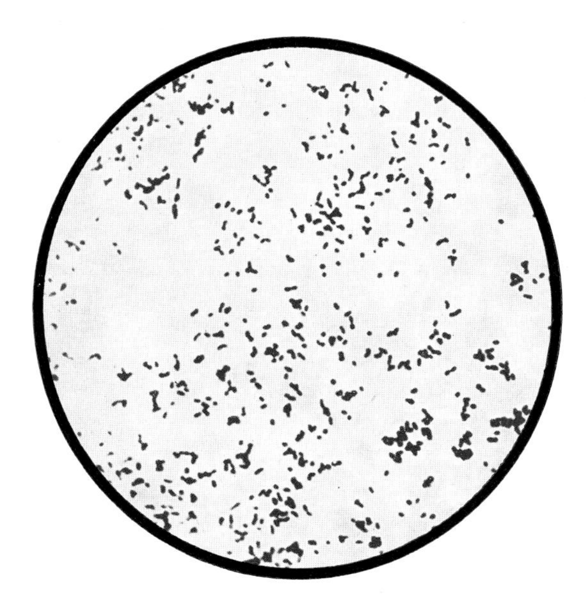

Fig. 86.

× **1250.** *Gram's stain.*

Film of culture of **Brucella melitensis**—a small Gram-negative cocco-bacillus of varying size. Note that magnification is × 1250.

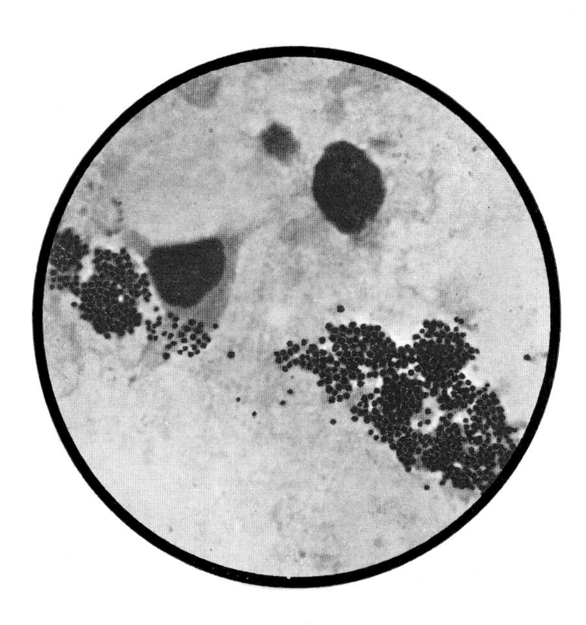

Fig. 87.

× **1250.** *Gram's stain.*

Smear from stomach of calf showing **Brucella abortus**—a small cocco-bacillus. In this case the organisms are practically all in coccal form.

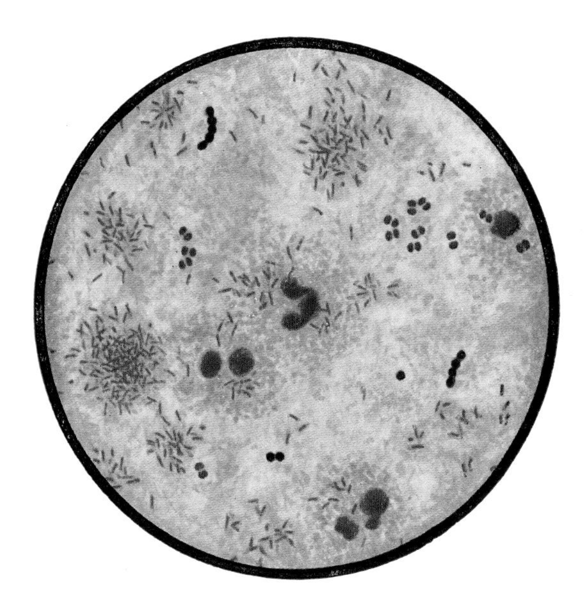

FIG. 88.

× **1000.** *Gram's stain.*

Film of sputum showing Gram-negative **Hæmophilus influenzæ** (**Pfeiffer's bacillus**), **Diplococcus catarrhalis** and a Gram-positive streptococcus. Note the small size of H. influenzæ and arrangement in clumps.

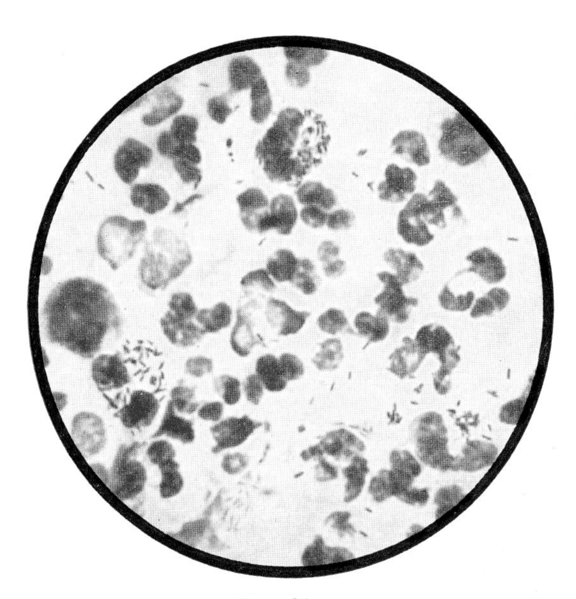

FIG. 89.

× **1000.** *Gram's stain.*

Film of conjunctival exudate showing **Koch-Week's bacillus** (**Hæmophilus conjunctivitidis**) a short slender Gram-negative bacillus morphologically identical with H. influenzæ. Note intracellular position of the organism in polymorph leucocytes.

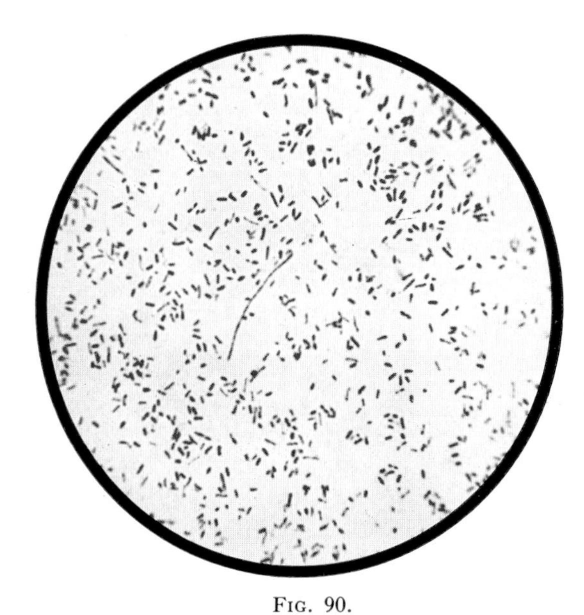

FIG. 90.

× **1000.** *Gram's stain.*

Film of culture of **Hæmophilus influenzæ**—a small Gram-negative straight bacillus. Note marked pleomorphism from very short coccal to long, filamentous forms.

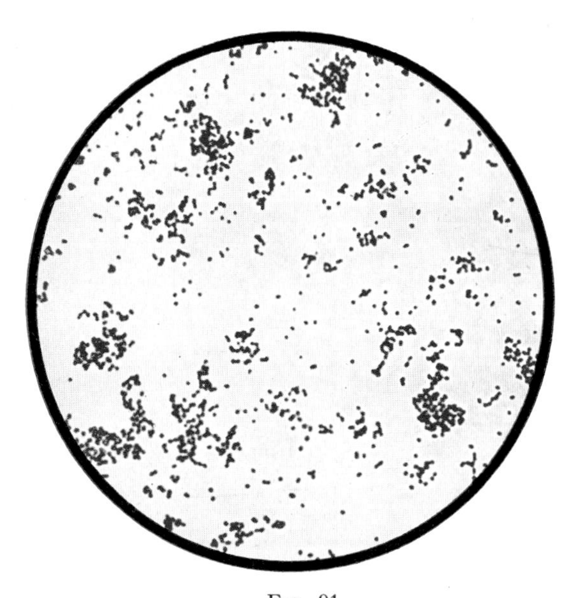

FIG. 91.

× **1000.** *Gram's stain.*

Film of culture of **Hæmophilus pertussis**—a very small Gram-negative oval cocco-bacillus less pleomorphic than H. influenzæ (cf., Fig. 90).

Needs X & V factors in blood
e.g. Coenzyme I & Haematin

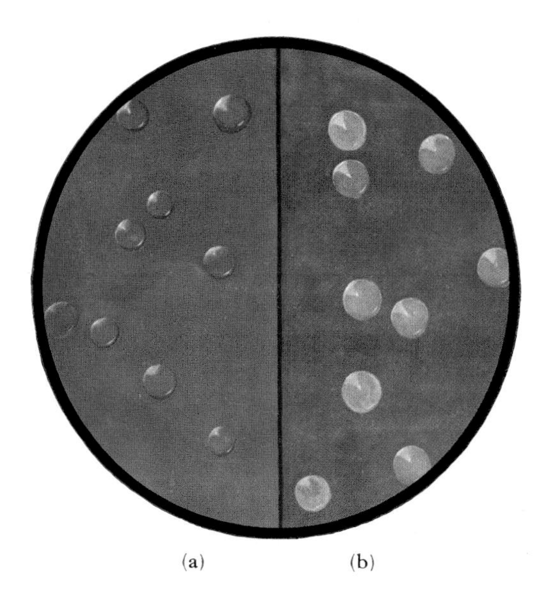

FIG. 92.

× **7½**.

(a) Enlarged colonies of **H. influenzæ** on **blood agar** medium, 2 days old, magnified 7½ times, showing typical clear " dew-drop " appearance.

(b) Enlarged colonies of **H. influenzæ** on **boiled blood** medium. Note that they are larger and not so clear as in (a).

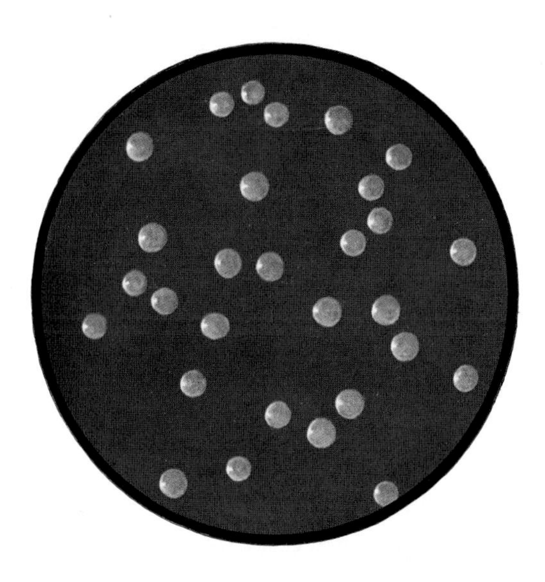

FIG. 93.

× **5.**

Enlarged colonies of **Hæmophilus pertussis** on Bordet-Gengou blood medium—5 days old, magnified 5 times. Colonies have the characteristic bright metallic appearance.

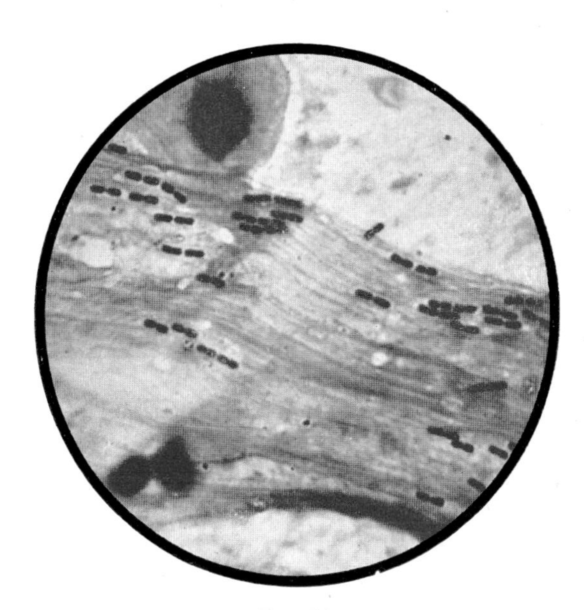

FIG. 94.

× **1000.** *Gram's stain.*

Film of conjunctival exudate from case of conjunctivitis due to **Hæmophilus lacunatus** (**Bacillus of Morax and Axenfeld**)—a short, thick, Gram-negative, diplo-bacillus.

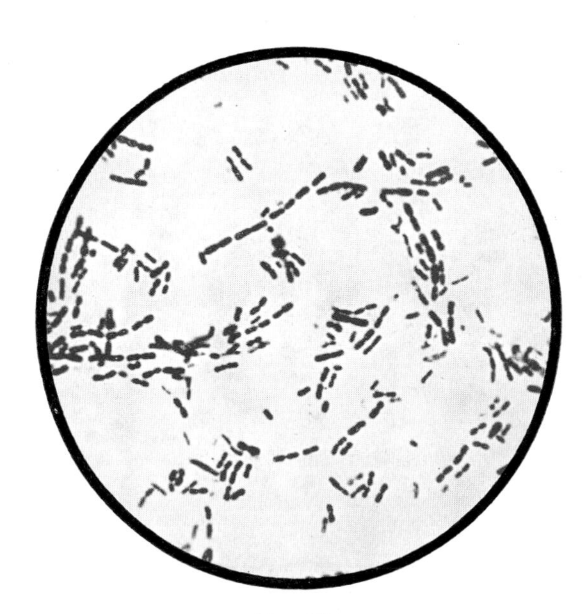

FIG. 95.

× **1000.** *Gram's stain.*

Film of culture of **H. lacunatus** on Lœffler's serum medium showing short Gram-negative bacilli in pairs and short chains; very short coccal forms are also seen.

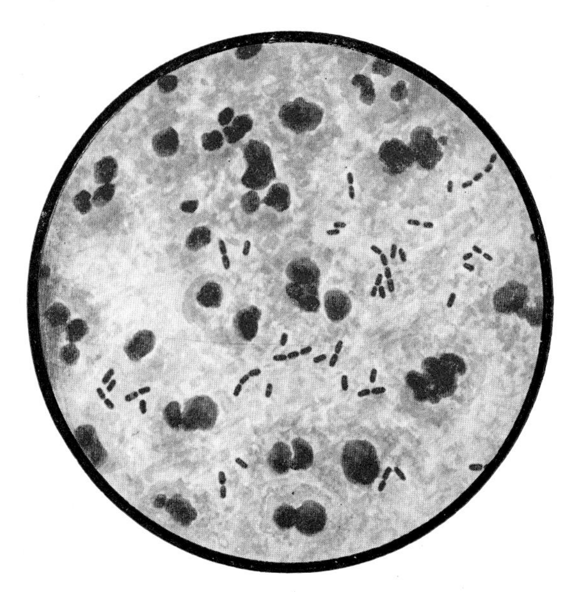

FIG. 96.

× **1000** *Methylene blue stain.*

Film of pus from soft sore (Ulcus molle) showing **Hæmophilus ducreyi**—a short broad bacillus seen singly, in pairs and short chains (streptobacillus).

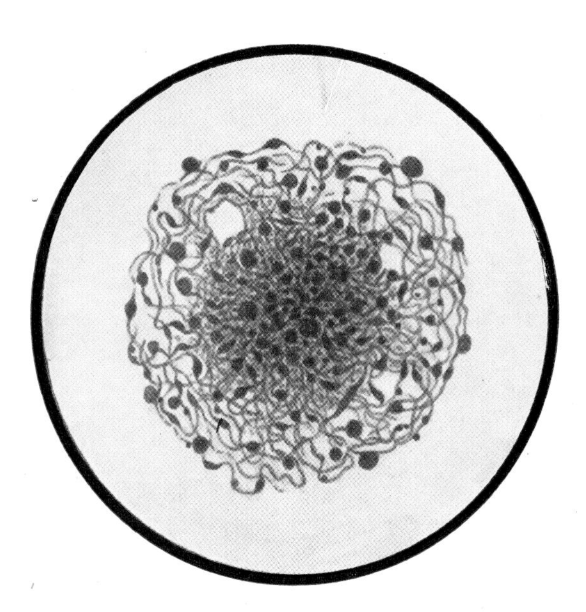

FIG. 97.

× **1000** *Polychrome methylene blue stain.*

Impression colony of **Haverhillia moniliformis** (**Streptobacillus moniliformis**) on 10% serum agar; 24 hours old. Note pleomorphism, bacillary forms in chain formation, filamentous forms, fusiform dilatations and bulbous lateral swellings, which are characteristic.

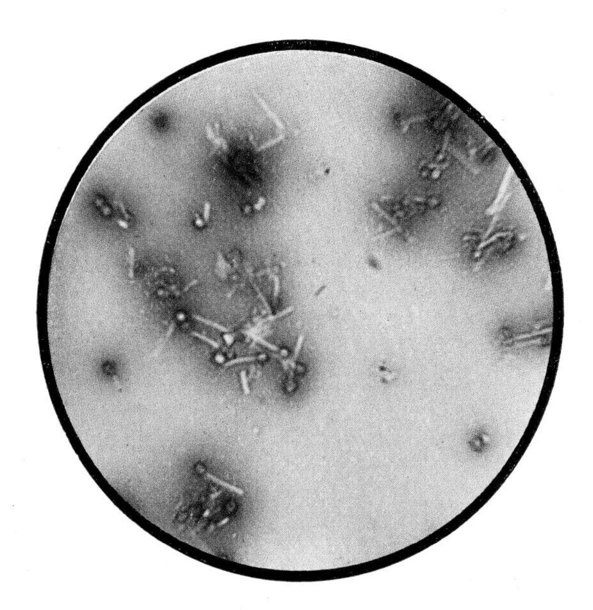

FIG. 98.

× **1000.** *Carbol-fuchsin nigrosin method.*

Film of culture of **Tetanus bacillus (Clostridium tetani)** showing characteristic "drum-stick" organisms—long thin straight bacillus with large terminal, spherical, bulging spore: some spores are also lying free.

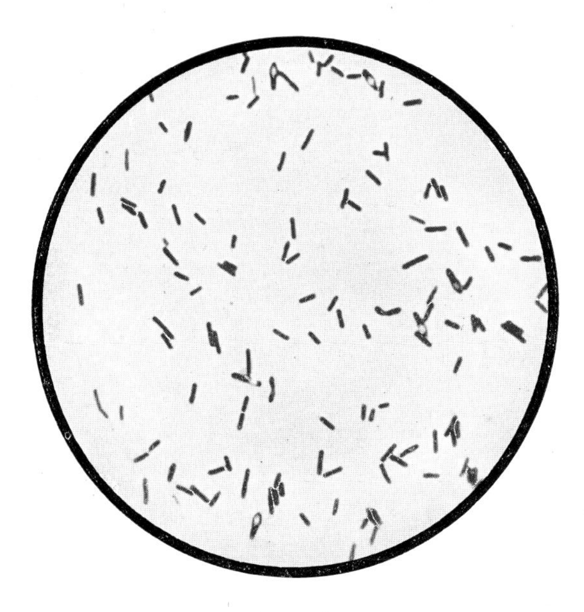

FIG. 99.

× **1000.** *Gram's stain.*

Film of culture of **Clostridium botulinum**—Gram-positive sporing bacillus with rounded ends occurring singly or in pairs: spores subterminal, oval and slightly bulging.

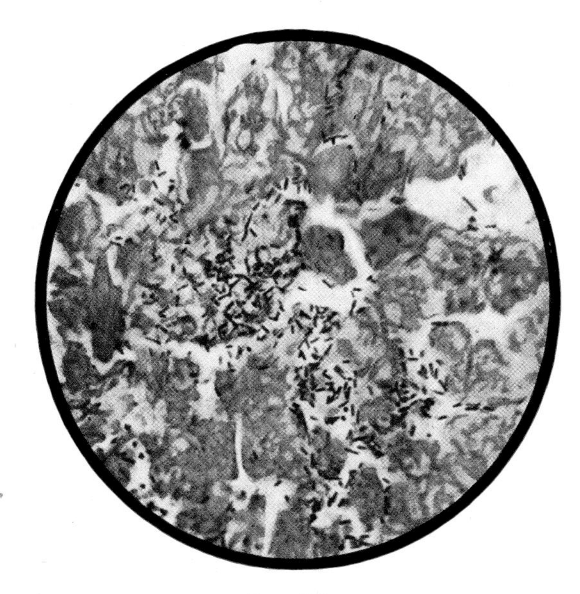

FIG. 100.

× **500.** *Gram's stain.*

Section of human muscle from case of gas gangrene showing **Bacillus welchii** (**Clostridium welchii**). Note the œdematous swelling of the muscle and separation of muscle fibres by formation of gas.

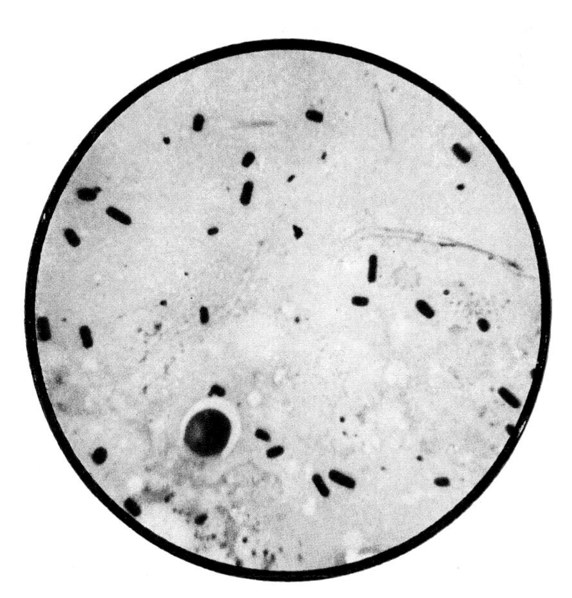

FIG. 101.

× **1000.** *Gram's stain.*

Smear made from muscle in same case as in Fig. 100, showing **Clostridium welchii**—a relatively large, straight Gram-positive bacillus with rounded ends. Note the variable length of the bacilli and absence of spores.

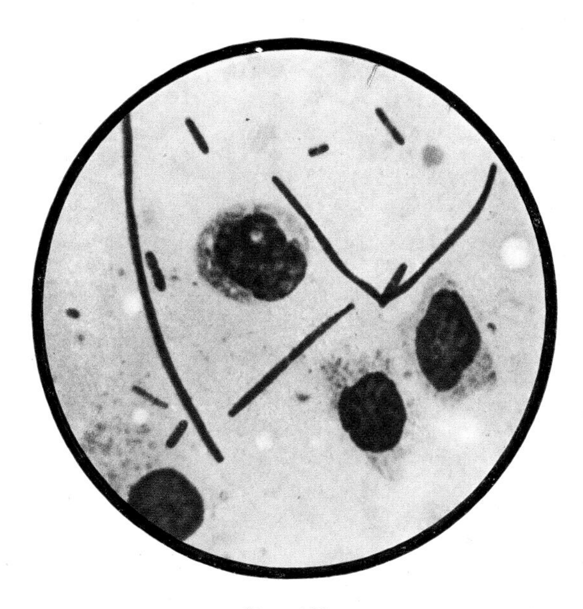

FIG. 102.

× **1000.** *Leishman's stain.*

Smear from liver of experimental animal showing Gram-positive, bacillary and filamentous forms of **Clostridium septicum** (**Vibrion septique**). This organism is found in Gas Gangrene of human beings and is the cause of Braxy in sheep and some cases of Black-leg in cattle and sheep.

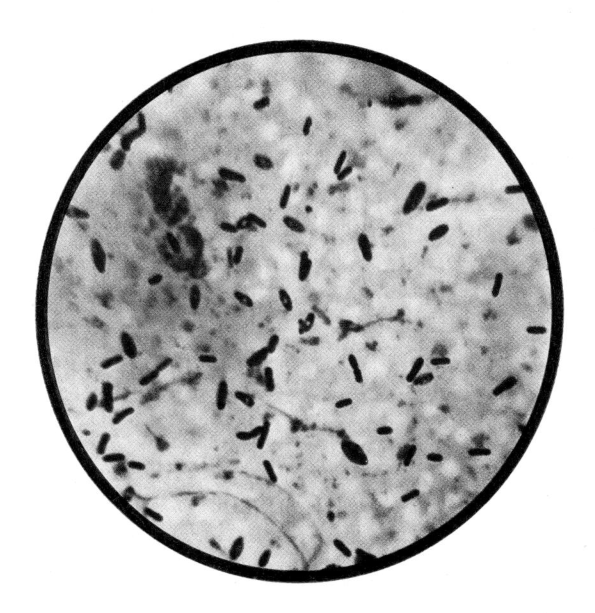

FIG. 103.

× **1000.** *Gram's stain.*

Smear of subcutaneous exudate at site of inoculation of experimental animal showing **Clostridium septicum** some of which show central spores. Large swollen lemon-shaped forms (**citron bodies**) are also seen.

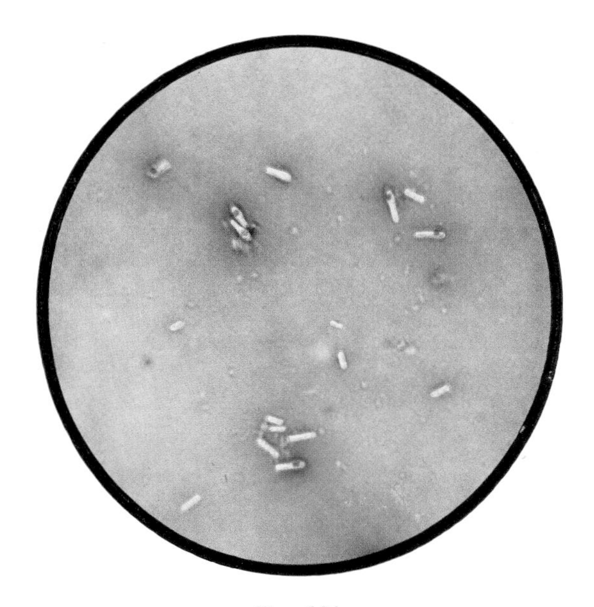

Fig. 104.

× **1000.** *Carbol-fuchsin-nigrosin stain.*

Film of culture of **Clostridium sporogenes**—a relatively large bacillus with oval subterminal spore, stained red.

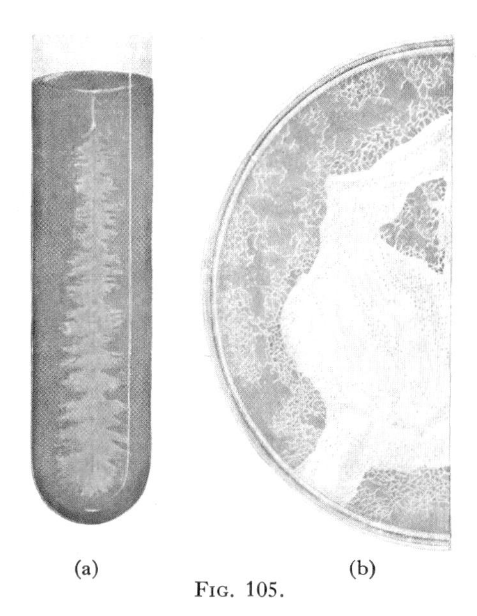

(a) (b)

FIG. 105.

Cultures of **Tetanus bacillus.**

(a) Agar stab culture showing growth with lateral spikes which are longest in the deepest part of the medium. Note absence of growth at the surface.
(b) Agar plate culture, under anærobic conditions, showing long branching projections from the edges of the main growth.

(a) (b)

Fig. 106.

Cultures of sporing anærobic bacilli in cooked meat medium.

(a) **Clostridium welchii** showing **saccharolytic** action with reddening and no digestion of the meat. Note that the pieces of meat are still quite distinctly seen.

(b) **Clostridium sporogenes** showing **proteolytic** action with blackening and digestion of the meat. The pieces of meat are indistinct owing to digestion.

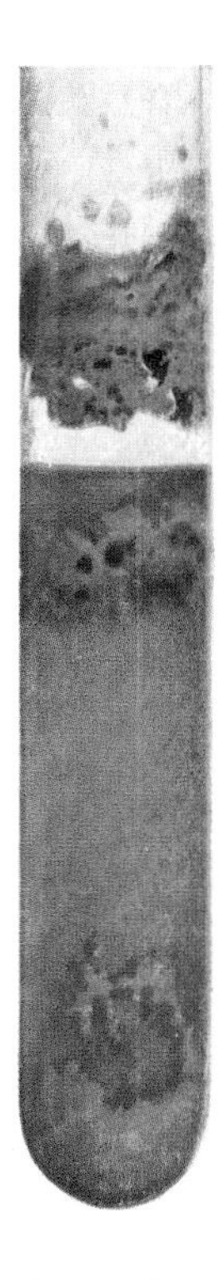

Fig. 107.

Anærobic culture of **Clostridium welchii** in anærobic litmus milk showing the characteristic **"stormy" clot.** Note the pink colour of the clot owing to formation of acid. Part of the clot has been blown out of the liquid owing to great production of gas. The clear yellowish liquid is the whey of the milk.

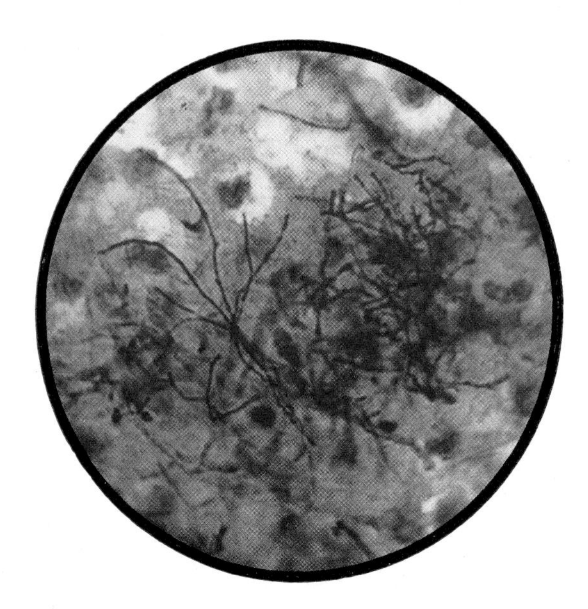

FIG. 108.

× **1000.** *Gram's stain.*

Film of pus from actinomycotic lesion in neck showing **Actinomyces**—Gram-positive branching streptothrix filaments with bacillary and coccal forms.

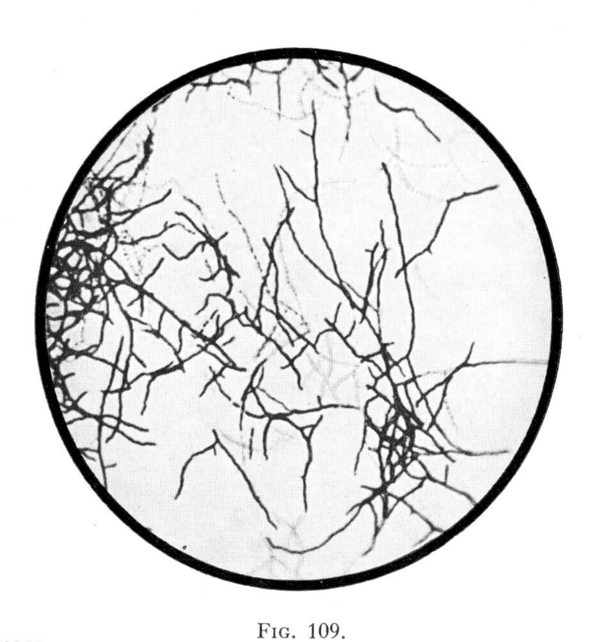

FIG. 109.

× **1000.** *Gram's stain.*

Film of culture of **Actinomyces** of **ærobic** (**Boström**) strain showing Gram-positive streptothrix, branching dichotomously, and bacillary and coccal forms.

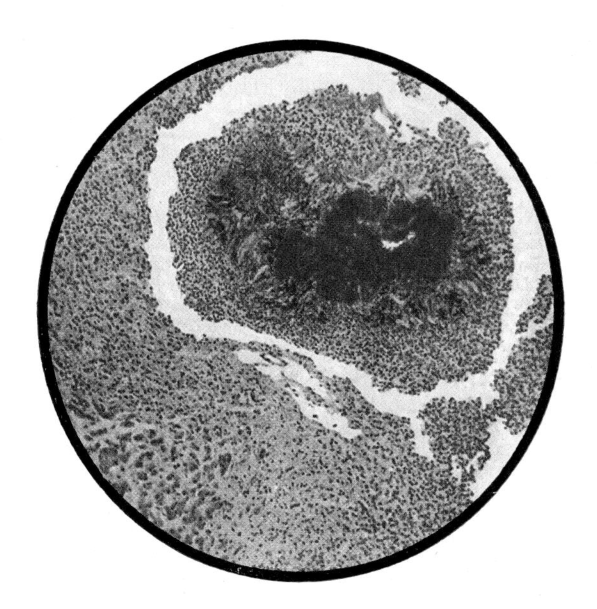

FIG. 110.

× **75.** *Gram's stain.*

Section of human liver under low-power showing **Actinomycotic abscess** with dense mass of Gram-positive streptothrix stained violet.

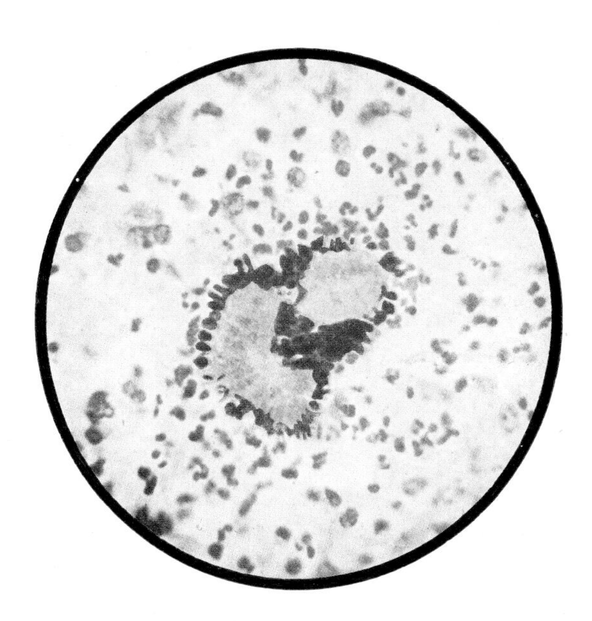

FIG. 111.

× **500.** *Modified Ziehl-Neelsen stain.*

Section of ox-tongue showing a colony of **actinomyces** in which the formation of clubs (stained red) is well seen.

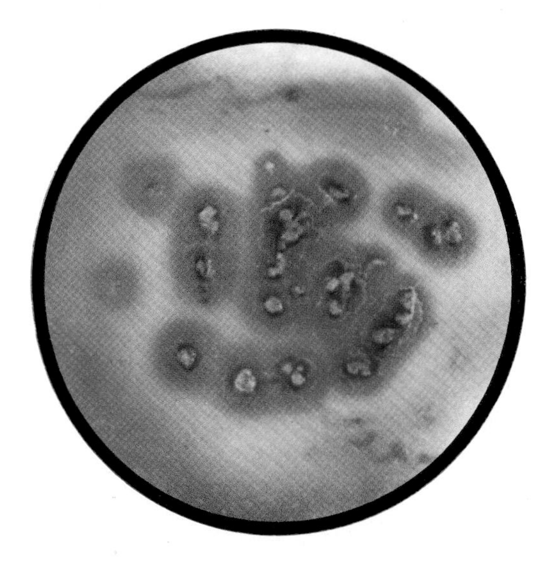

FIG. 112.

× **2.**

Pus from Actinomycotic abscess spread out on a glass plate showing **sulphur-yellow granules** twice their actual size.

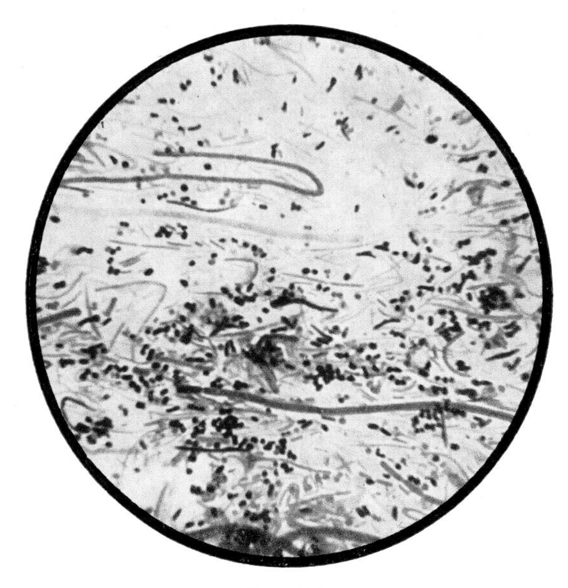

FIG. 113.

× **1000.** *Gram's stain.*

Film of material taken from between the teeth of normal mouth showing long non-branching threads of Gram-positive **Leptothrix buccalis.** Older Gram-negative filaments are also seen as well as Gram-positive and Gram-negative cocci and bacilli.

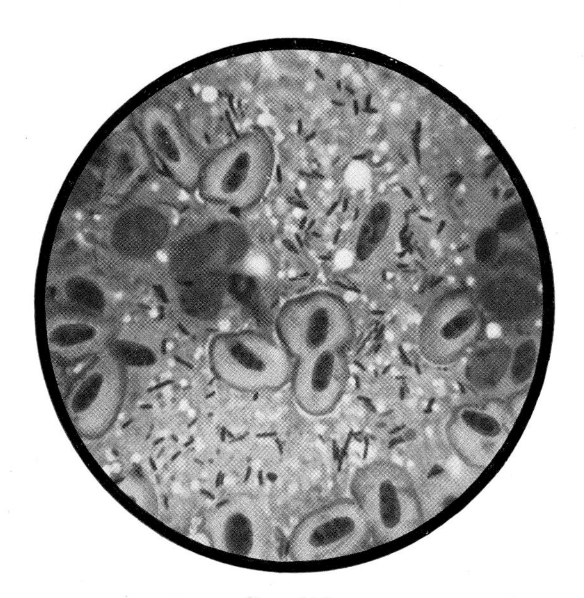

FIG. 114.

× **1000.** *Gram's stain.*

Smear from spleen of experimentally inoculated pigeon showing **Bacillus rhusiopathiæ** (**Erysipelothrix rhusiopathiæ**) the causative organism of swine Erysipelas and Erysipeloid (" diamond disease ") in human beings. The bacillus is straight, slender, Gram-positive and varies greatly in length. Note also the presence of a Gram-negative coliform organism the result of a terminal infection; also oval nucleated erythrocytes of the bird.

SYPHILIS

1. Fontana's silver staining method.
2. Wassermann Test. (Complement fixation)

Primary		Secondary	Tertiary
Chancre 10-14 days after exposure	→	Disapp: of Chancre	CNS Stage
W.R ±		Skin lesions 6-8 weeks after exposure	2-30 years after exposure
		W.R. ++	W.R. ±

3. Flocculation test
4. Kahn verification test.

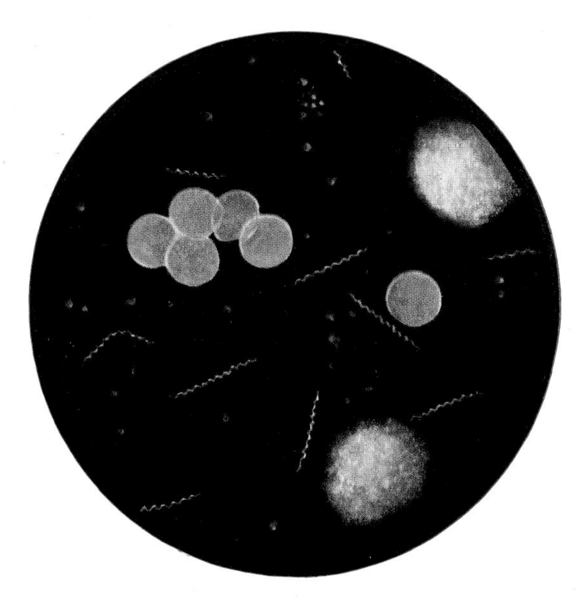

Fig. 115.

× **1000.** *Dark-ground illumination.*

Serous exudate from primary lesion of Syphilis showing living **Treponema pallidum,** red blood corpuscles and leucocytes. Note extreme delicacy of the Spirochætal filament and its small regular closely-set coils : one organism shows flexion.

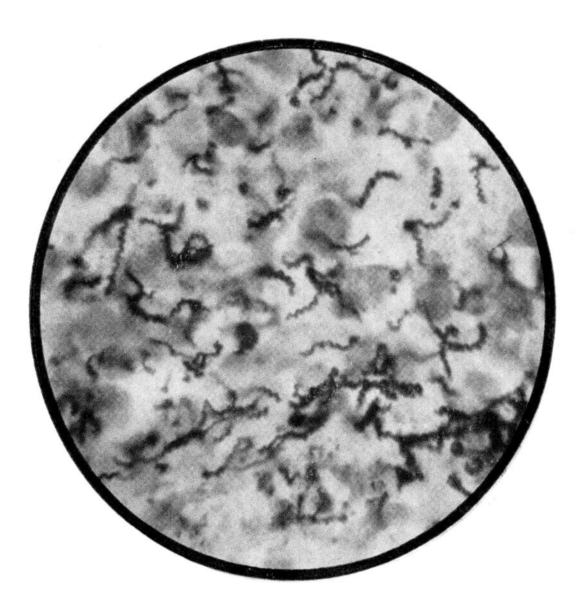

Fig. 116.

× **1000.** *Dobell's modification of* **Levaditi's** *stain and basic fuchsin counter-stain.*

Section of fœtal liver from case of Congenital Syphilis showing **Treponema pallidum** in large numbers. Note how much thicker the spirochætes look than in Fig. 115, owing to the deposit of silver on them.

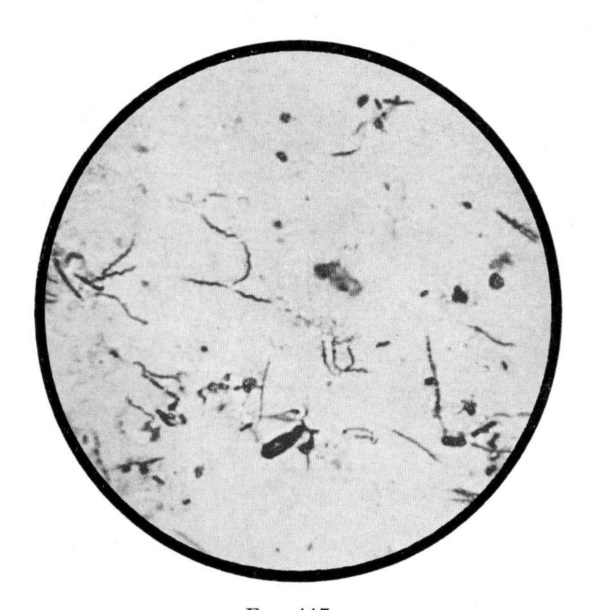

FIG. 117.

× **1250.** *Dilute carbol-fuchsin stain.*

Film of material taken from between the teeth of apparently normal mouth showing a short treponema probably **Treponema microdentium.**

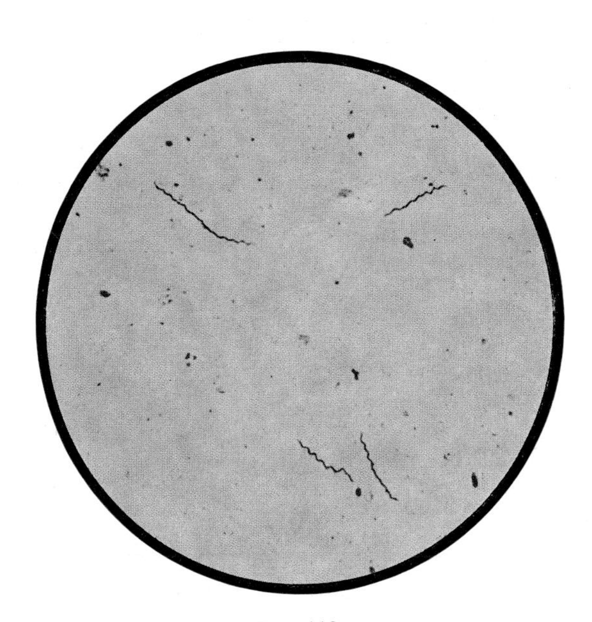

FIG. 118.

× **1000.** *Fontana's stain.*

Film of material from rabbit's genitals showing **Treponema cuniculi** which is morphologically similar to Treponema pallidum.

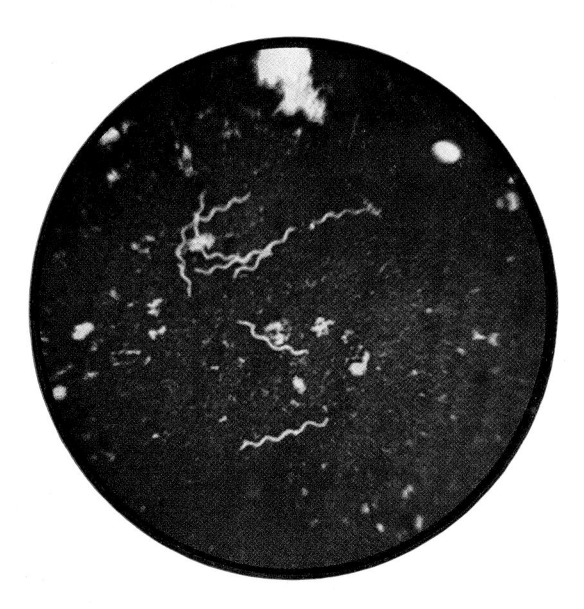

FIG. 119.

× **1000.** *Indian ink method.*

Film of material taken from between the teeth of normal mouth showing **Borrelia refringens** unstained against dark back-ground of Indian ink. Note relatively thick filament with wide coils.

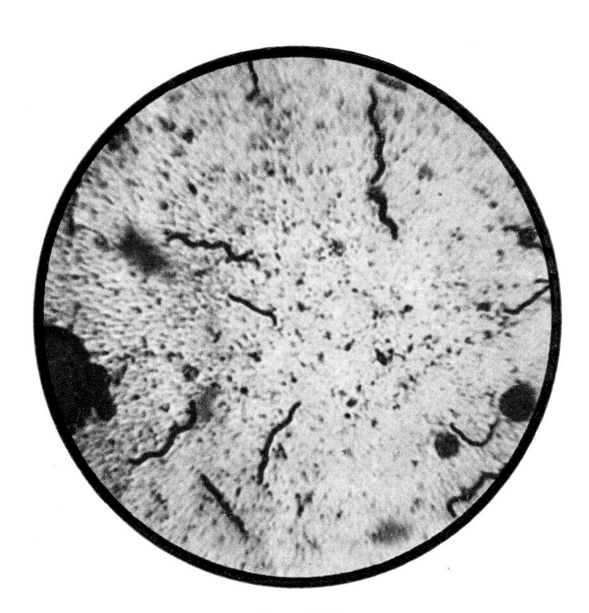

FIG. 120.

× **1000.** *Fontana's stain.*

Film of material taken from between the teeth of normal mouth showing **Borrelia refringens.** Note that the spirochætes are thickened by deposit of silver on them (cf., Fig. 119). The irregularity of the coils is due to the heating in fixation and staining.

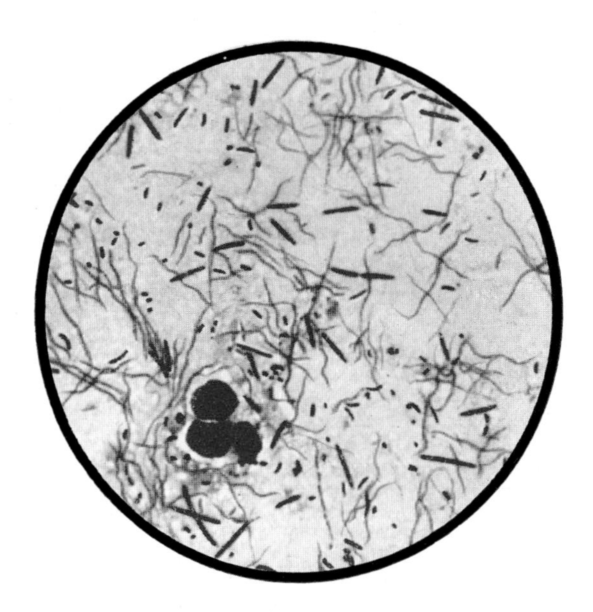

FIG. 121.

× **1250.** *Dilute carbol-fuchsin stain.*

Film from mouth of case of ulcerative gingivitis showing **Borrelia vincenti** and **Bacillus fusiformis.** Note large numbers of spirochætes closely resembling Borrelia refringens but often smaller in size, together with large fusiform bacilli with pointed ends and often seen in pairs.

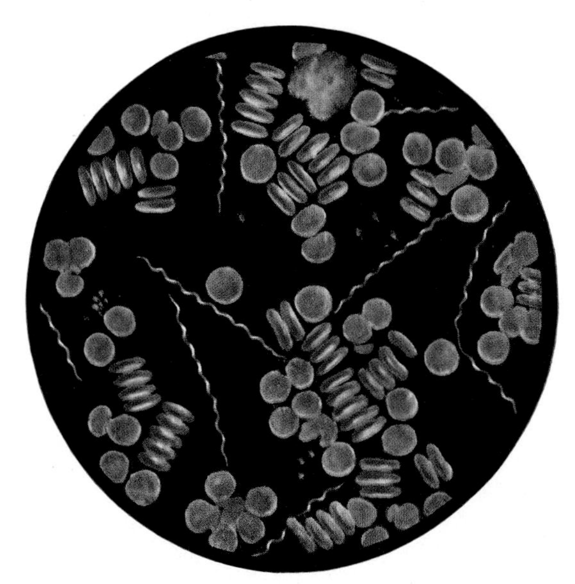

FIG. 122.

× **1000.** *Dark-ground illumination.*

Blood of mouse showing living **Borrelia duttoni** the causative organism of West-African tick-borne Relapsing fever. Note glistening white spirochæte with regular wide coils; to the right division is seen taking place.

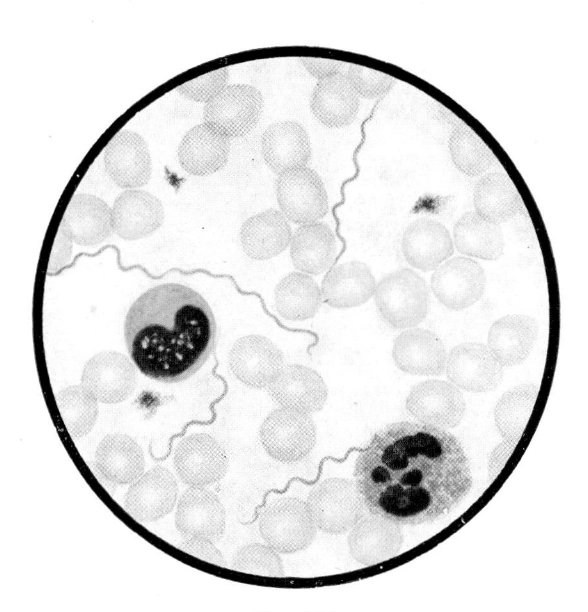

FIG. 123.

× **1000.** *Leishman's stain.*

Blood film from case of Relapsing fever showing **Borrelia recurrentis or obermeieri.** Note one spirochæte near the mononucleated leucocyte about to divide; in stained preparations the spirality of the organism is less regular than in the fresh dark-ground preparation (cf., Fig. 122).

FIG. 124.

× **1000.** *Dark-ground illumination.*

Culture of living **Leptospira ictero-hæmorrhagiæ** in Fletcher's medium showing the different shapes which the leptospira commonly assumes during life. Note the very fine coils and characteristic hooked ends. The brownish granular material of the background is Fletcher's medium.

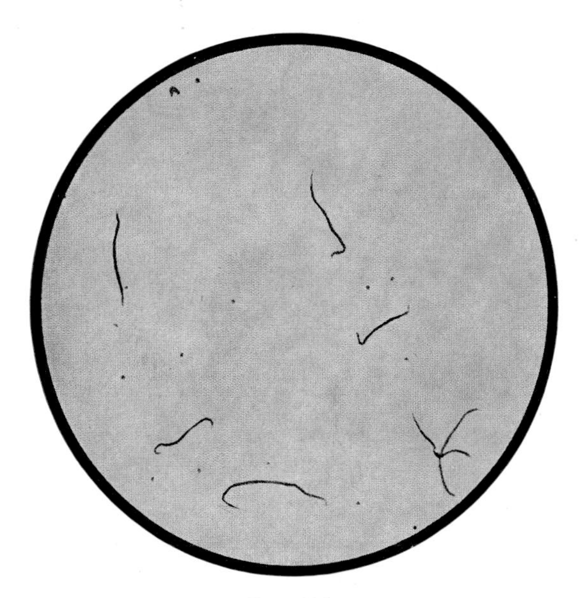

FIG. 125.

× **1000.** *Fontana's stain.*

Film of culture of **Leptospira ictero-hæmorrhagiæ** in Fletcher's medium stained with silver nitrate (cf., Fig. 124). Note the dead appearance of the organism with tendency to straighten out at the ends.

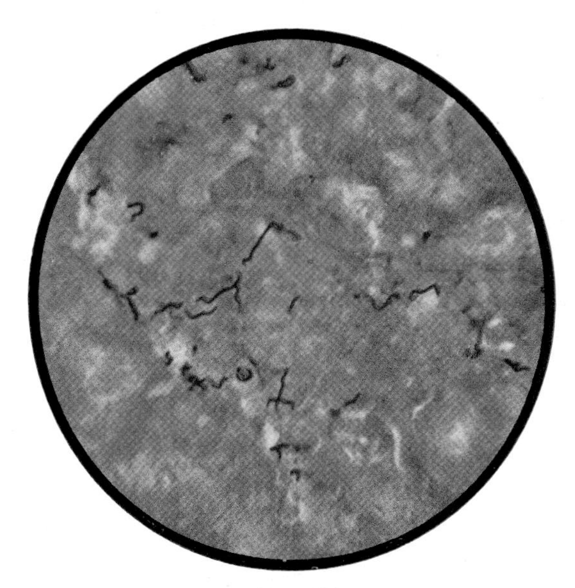

FIG. 126.

× **1000.** *Dobell's modification of Levaditi's stain.*

Section of rat's kidney showing **Leptospira ictero-hæmorrhagiæ.** Note the shrinkage of the spirochætes owing to fixation and heating in preparation of section as compared with the living organism in Fig. 124.

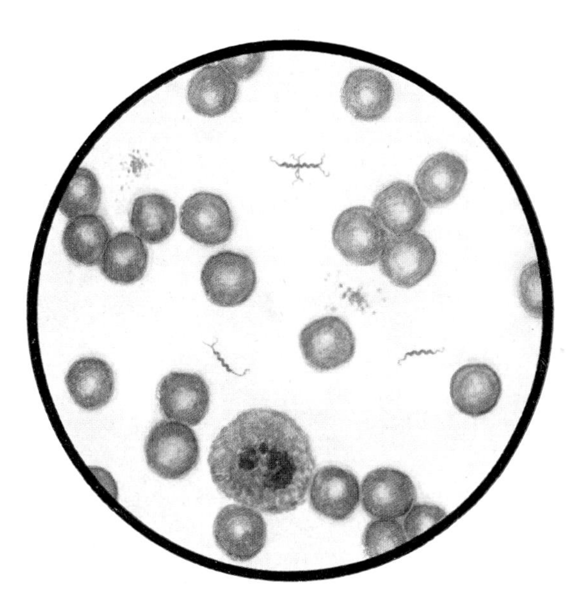

FIG. 127.

× **1000.** *Adachi's modification of Giemsa's stain.*

Blood film from mouse showing **Spirillum minus** of **Rat-bite fever** with terminal flagella. What appears to be a single thick flagellum is in reality 5-7 very fine flagella sticking together. At the upper part of film a Spirillum is in process of division.

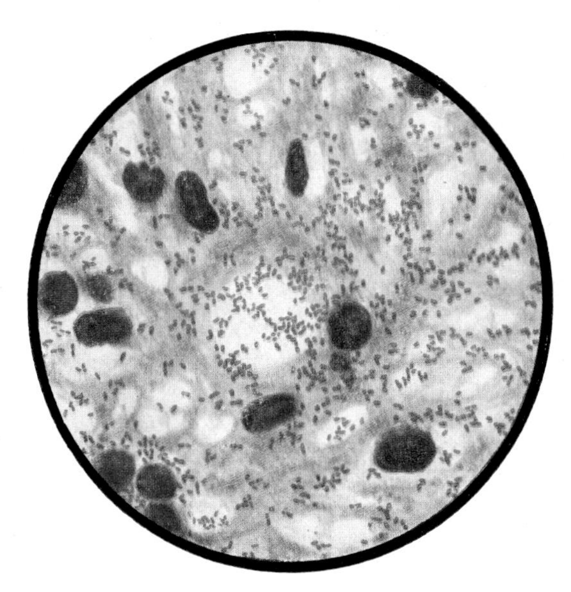

Fig. 128.

× **1000.** *Giemsa's stain.*

Film of culture of **Rickettsia prowazeki** of **Typhus fever** in yolk-sac of fertile hen egg. Note the small size ($0{\cdot}3\mu$) of the organism which occurs chiefly as diplococcal and very short rod-shaped bodies.

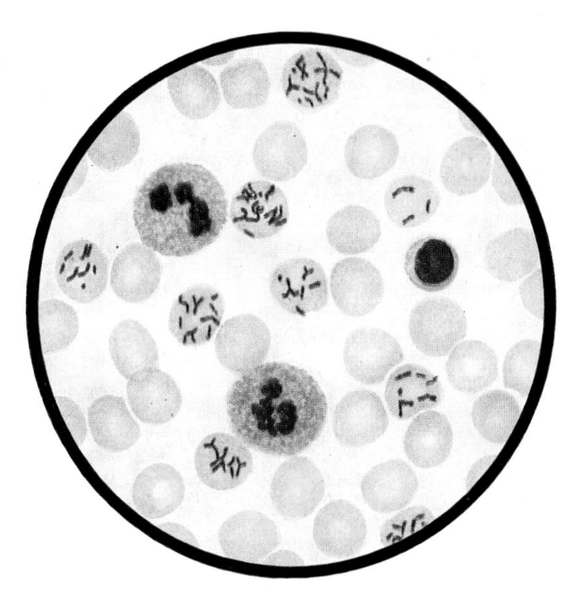

Fig. 129.

× **1000.** *Leishman's stain.*

Blood film from case of Oroya fever showing **Bartonella bacilliformis** adhering to the erythrocytes. The organism occurs in coccal and rod-shaped forms with slightly thickened ends and often arranged like a Y.

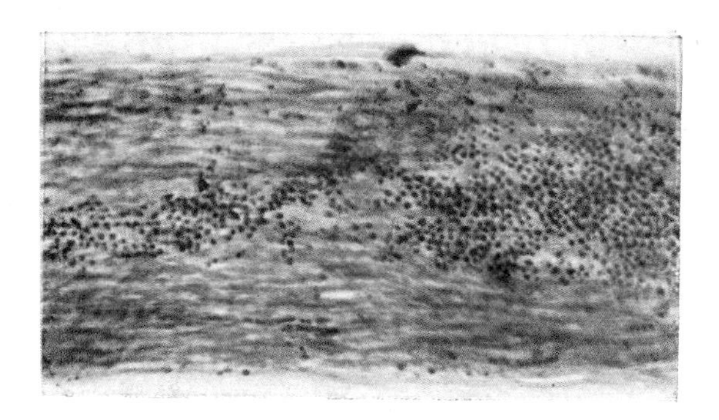

FIG. 130.
× **350.** *Martinotti's stain (Lith-carb. and toluidin blue).*
Scalp hair showing small-spore human ringworm fungus (**Microsporon audouini**). Note threads of mycelium running longitudinally and splitting up the substance of the hair and a sheath of small round spores forming a mosaic on the surface of the hair.

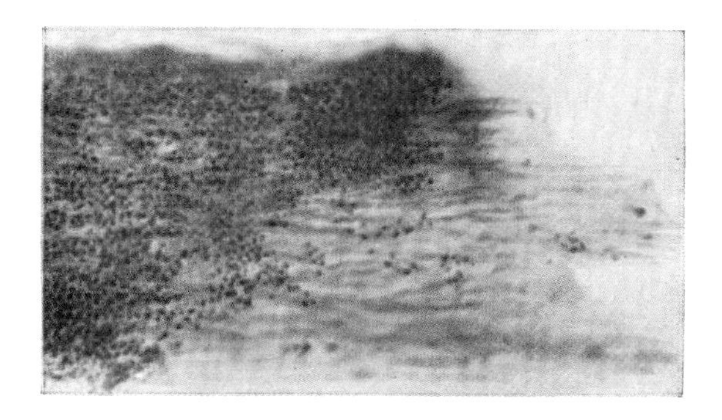

FIG. 131.
× **350.** *Martinotti's stain.*
Same as in Fig. 130, showing the mosaic of small spores on the surface and brush-like broken free end of the hair.

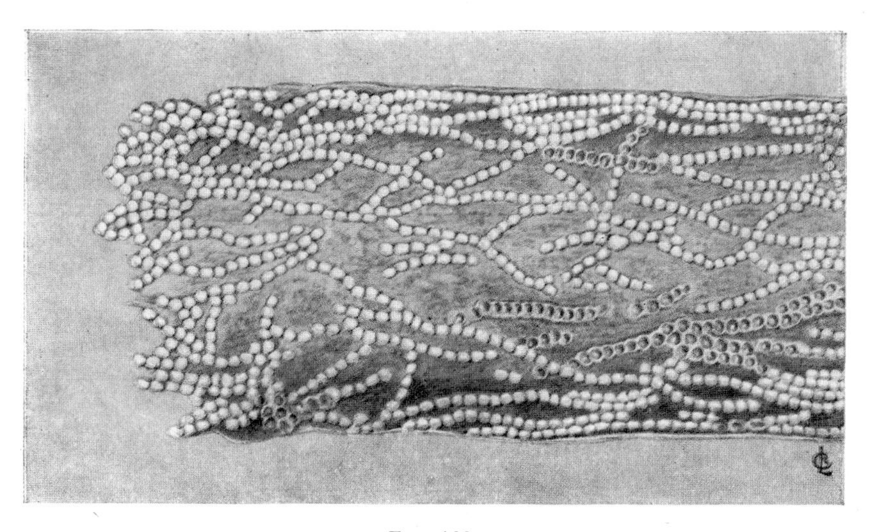

FIG. 132.

× **500.** *Wet preparation in Liq. potassæ.*

Scalp hair from case of large-spore ringworm due to **Trichophyton megalosporon** examined unstained. Note large square-cornered elongated spores running in chain formation inside the hair substance. The whole hair is somewhat softened and swollen by the action of the liq. potass. The broken free end of the hair is brush-like.

FIG. 133.

× **400.** *Wet preparation in Liq. potassæ.*

Human scalp hairs, **normal** (upper) and infected with **favus fungus** (lower) **Achorion schönleinii** examined unstained. The favus hair shows long threads of branching hyphæ running longitudinally through the hair substance; at the right end of hair, bubbles of air are seen being driven out of the hyphæ as the liq. potass. penetrates. This is characteristic of favus. Towards the other end of the hair a row of elongated arthrospores is visible. As the favus fungus does not grow through to the surface of the hair, the hair in favus does not break when pulled on as occurs in ringworm. Note also that in all hairs affected with ringworm or favus the medulla of the hair (visible in normal hair) cannot be seen.

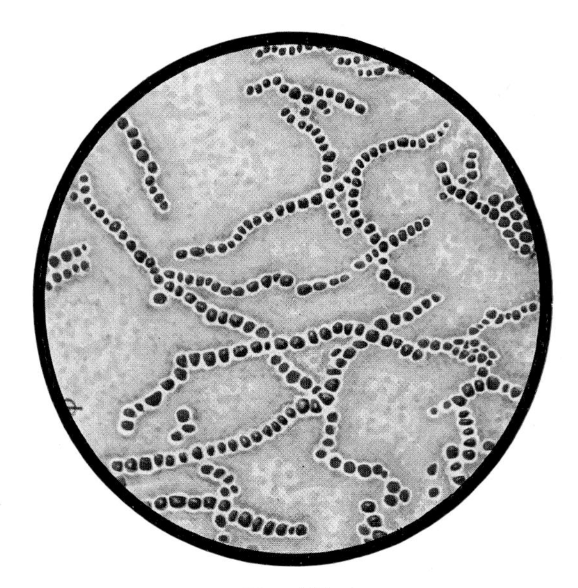

FIG. 134.

× **750.** *Wet preparation in Liq. potassæ.*

Piece of finger-nail showing **large-spore ringworm fungus (Trichophyton).** Note long rows of squarish spores.

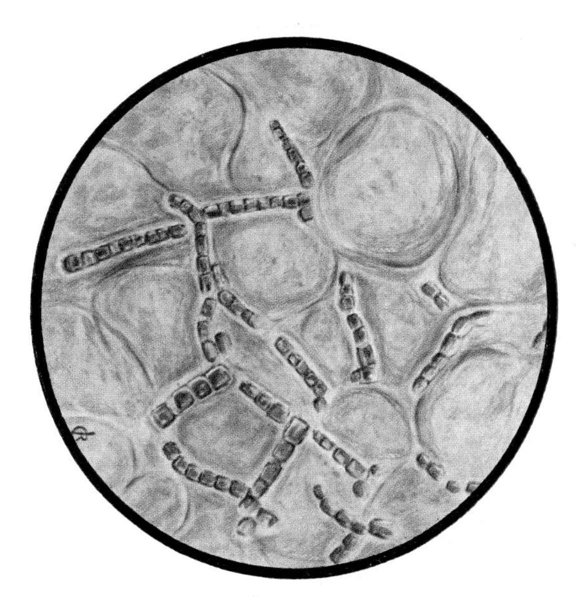

FIG. 135.

× **750.** *Wet preparation in Liq. potassæ.*

Skin scales from sole of foot showing the so-called **mosaic or "ghost" fungus**—rows of square-cornered elements which look like fungus spores and are found between the epithelial cells only. These on higher magnification can be seen to be crystals of cholesterol soluble in acetone. This appearance is not characteristic of ringworm and may be found in any chronic skin inflammation.

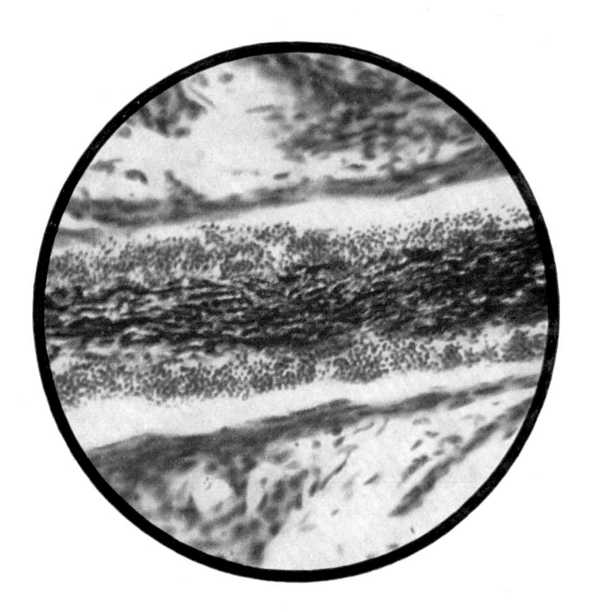

FIG. 136.

× **350.** *Hæmatoxylin and eosin stain.*

Section of hair in hair follicle of kitten suffering from **small-spore ringworm** (**Microsporon felinum**). Note how the substance of the hair is broken up by the fungus and the whole hair is surrounded by a sheath of small round spores exactly the same as in human small-spore ringworm (cf., Fig. 130).

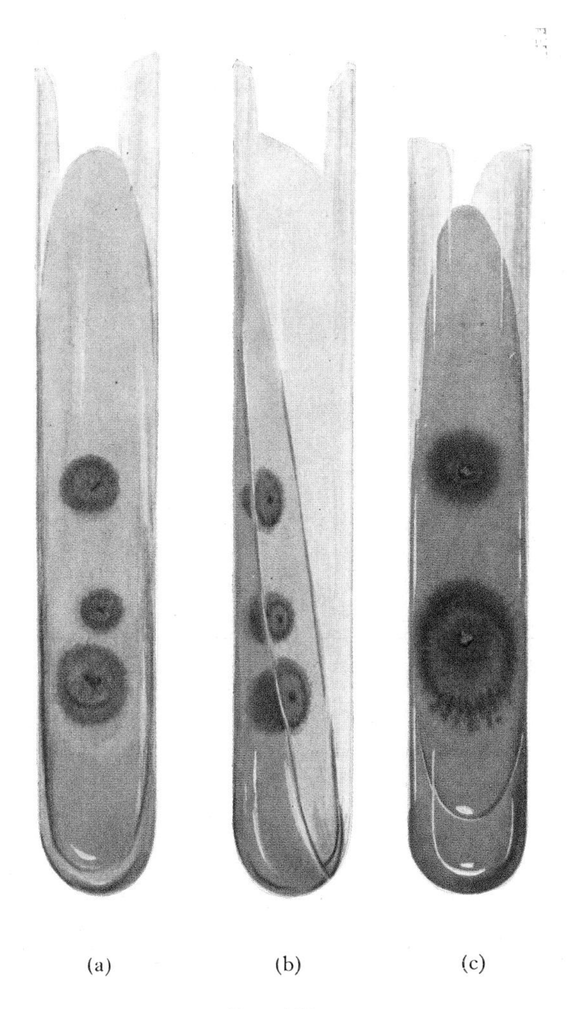

(a) (b) (c)

FIG. 137.

(a) and (b) Cultures, at room temperature, of cat small-spore ringworm fungus (**Microsporon felinum**) grown from a kitten's hair on glucose agar. Note the way in which the fungus has grown down into the medium.

(c) Culture, at room temperature, of horse small-spore ringworm fungus (**Microsporon equinum**) grown from the skin of a cavalry horse on glucose agar. The same fungus was also cultured from the rider of the horse.

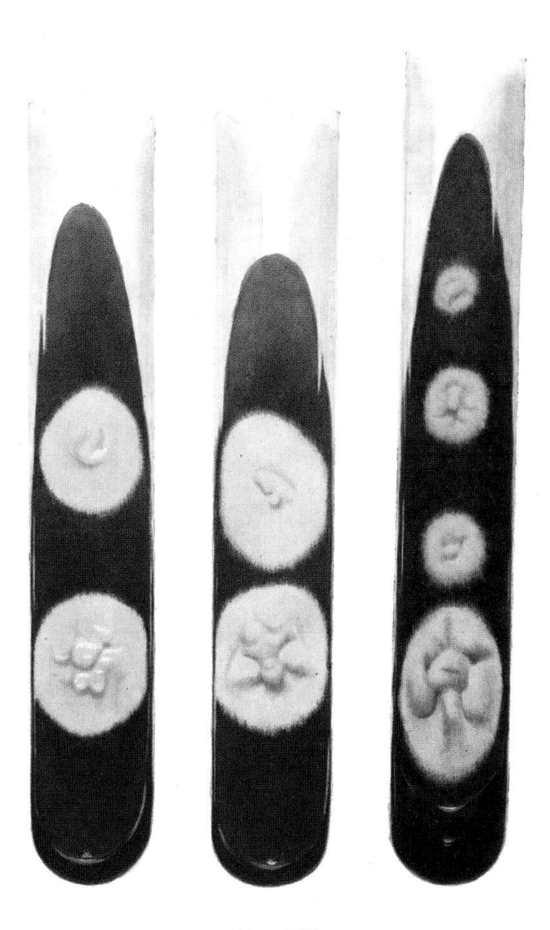

FIG. 138.

Cultures, at room temperature, of **large-spore ringworm fungi (Trichophytons)** grown from cases of ringworm of the finger-nails on Sabouraud's (original) maltose agar. They all show Trichophytons of the Rosaceum group. Note that all colonies of Trichophyton fungi are denser and more opaque than colonies of small-spore fungi (cf., Fig. 137).

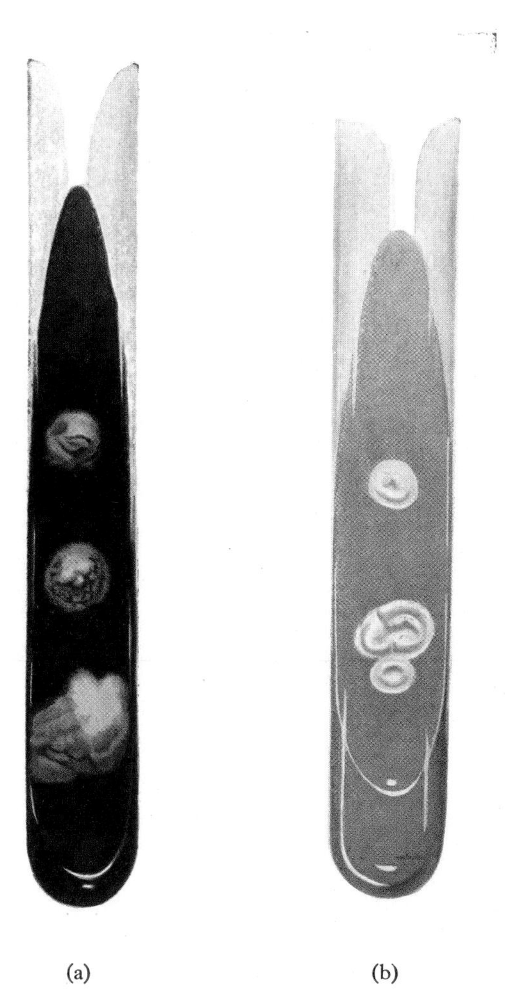

(a) (b)

FIG. 139.

(a) Culture, at room temperature from a case of **Dhobi itch,** of **Epidermophyton inguinale** (**floccosum**) on Sabouraud's (original) maltose agar. Note on the two lower colonies commencing mutation with the production of whitish fluffy growth on the top of the original growth.

(b) Culture, at room temperature, of **Achorion schönleinii,** from a case of human **Favus capitis,** on glucose agar. Note the depression in the centre of the growth similar to the hollow of the " scutulum " in the clinical lesion.

FIG. 140.
Culture of the **cat small-spore** ringworm fungus (**Microsporon felinum**) grown at room temperature for 3 months on Sabouraud's (original) maltose agar. Note the perfect symmetry of the growth and fine " hairy " appearance which is characteristic of the cultures of all small-spore ringworm fungi.

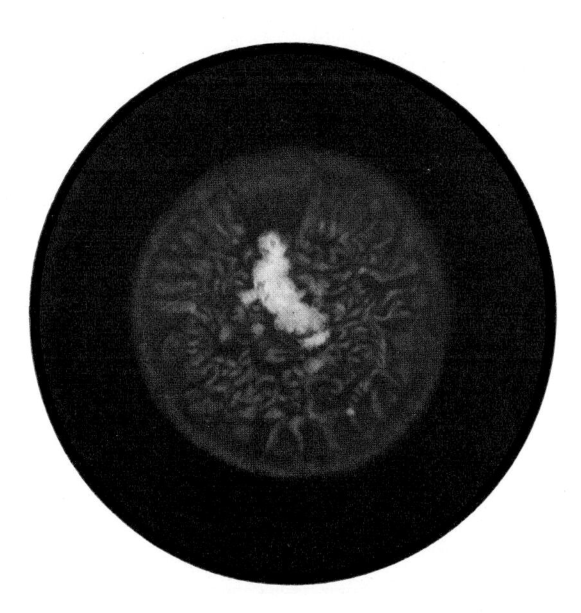

FIG. 141.
Culture on Sabouraud's (original) maltose agar, at room temperature for two months, of **Sporothrix schenkii** from a cutaneous lesion of **Sporotrichosis.** Note the dense wrinkled brown velvety growth with a white area of commencing mutation.

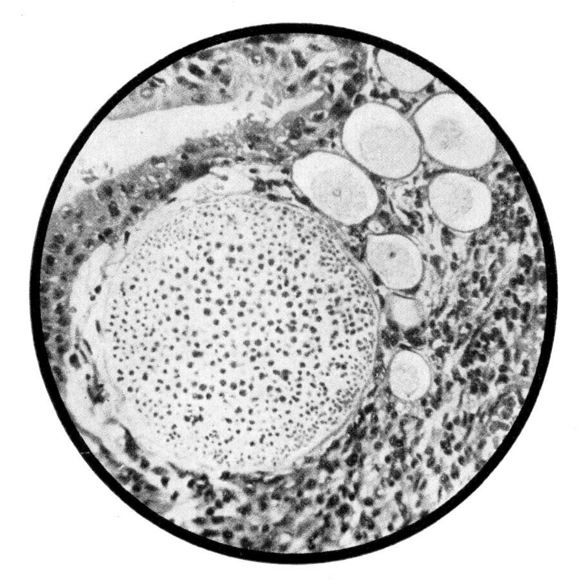

FIG. 142.

× **200.** *Hæmatoxylin and eosin stain.*

Section of granuloma from case of **Rhinosporidiosis** of the nose showing the causative fungus (**Rhinosporidium seeberi**). Note the large sporangium (190μ) filled with hundreds of spherical spores. The earlier stages in the development of sporangia are also seen.

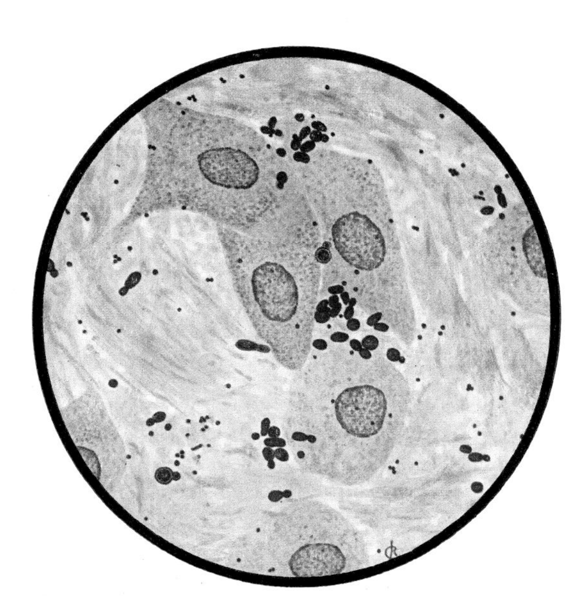

FIG. 143.

× **500.** *Leishman's stain.*

Scales from scalp of case of **Pityriasis capitis (dandruff)** showing **Pityrosporon seborrhœæ (ovale)**—a Gram-positive oval budding yeast belonging to the Cryptococcus (torula) group of fungi. Note the oval shape and large size of the fungus compared with the cocci.

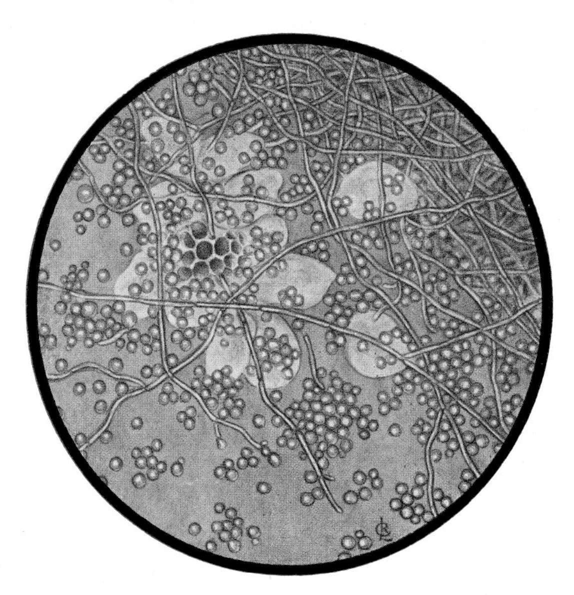

FIG. 144.

× **500.** *Wet preparation in Liq. potassæ.*

The edge of a patch of **Thrush** of the mucous membrane of the vagina showing **Monilia albicans** as long threads of hyphæ and rounded spores some of which show attached buds. Squamous epithelial cells from the mucous membrane are also seen.

FIG. 145.

× **1000.** *Gram's stain.*

Film of scraping from a patch of **Thrush** from baby's mouth showing **Monilia albicans** as long segments of Gram-positive hyphæ and oval yeast-like forms. Note also Gram-positive cocci most of which are streptococci (probably viridans) and compare the sizes of the fungus and the cocci.

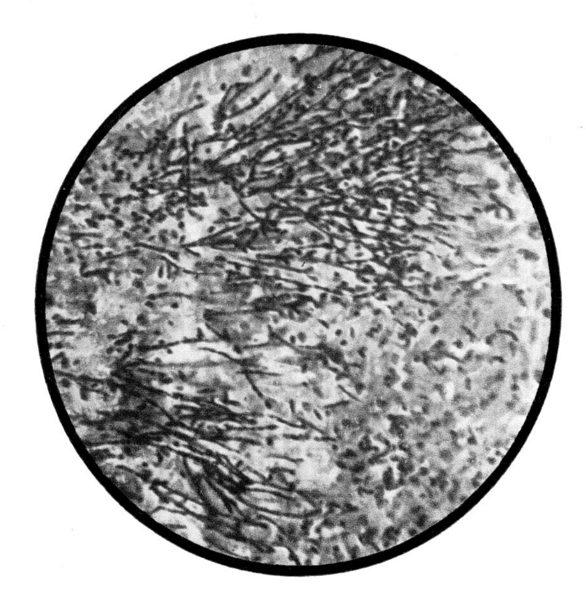

FIG. 146.

× **300.** *Gram's stain.*

Section of œsophageal wall in fatal case of **Thrush** (**Monilia albicans**) infection of mouth and respiratory tract in an infant. Note long threads of Gram-positive hyphæ and round and oval yeast forms penetrating into the wall of the œsophagus.

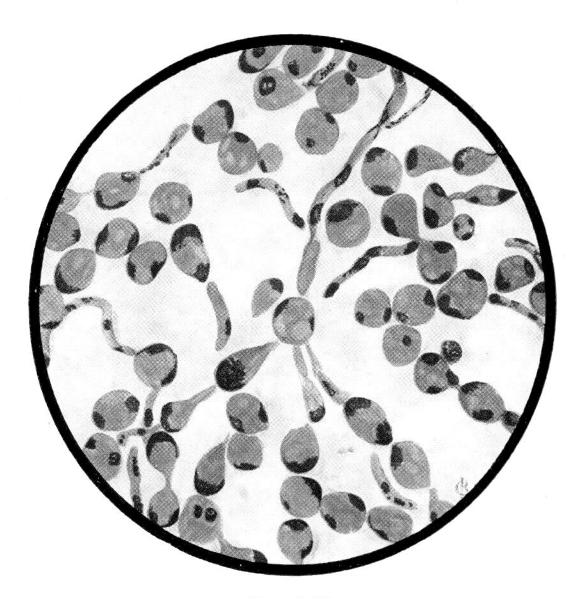

FIG. 147.

× **750.** *Muir's capsule stain.*

Film of culture of **Monilia albicans** in glucose broth showing short hyphal elements and roundish and oval yeast forms. Note that the pointed shape of some of the elements is an artefact produced in spreading and fixing the film. The red granular material in both hyphal and yeast forms is metachromatic material (Volutin). The minute nuclear body of the fungus does not stain by this method. The rounded light-coloured areas inside the fungus elements are glycogen vacuoles.

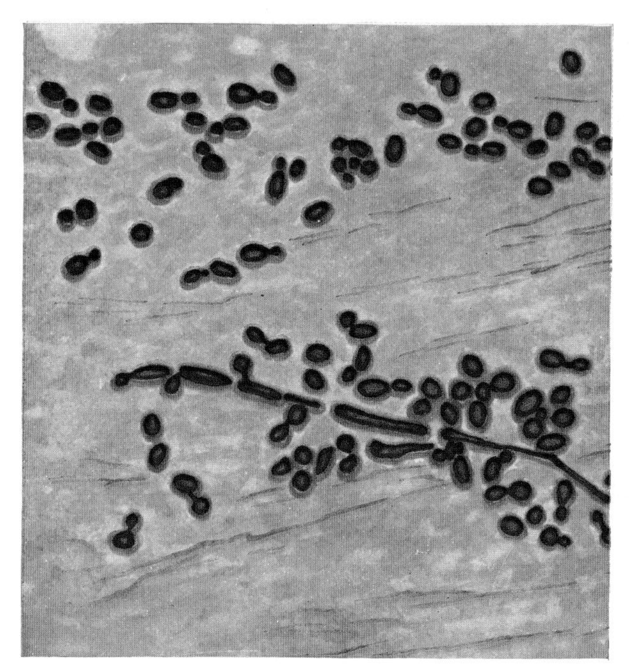

FIG. 148.

× **1000.** *Muir's capsule stain.*

Film of sputum showing **Thrush fungus** (**Monilia albicans**) with short hyphal threads and round or oval yeast forms some of which show buds. The presence of this fungus in a sputum does not necessarily mean that it is pathogenic.

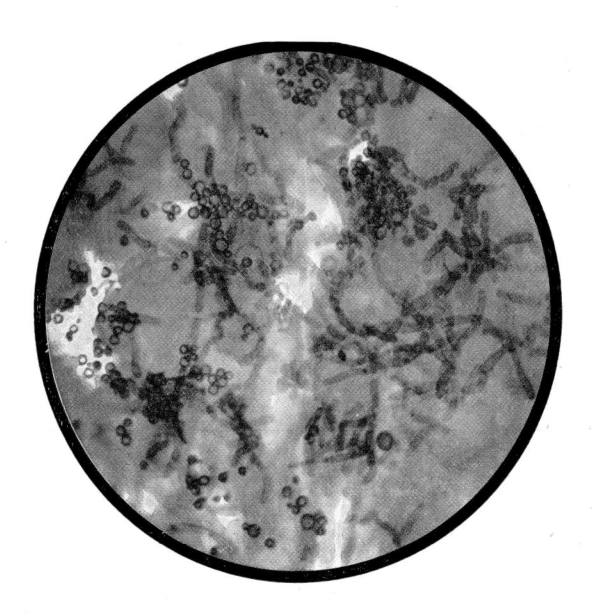

FIG. 149.

× **500.** *Borax methylene blue and carbol-fuchsin stain.*
Skin scraping from case of **Pityriasis versicolor** showing the causative fungus, **Malassezia (Microsporon) furfur,** consisting of short hyphal elements and the characteristic bunches of round yeast-like forms, some of which show small buds, arranged in groups like bunches of grapes.

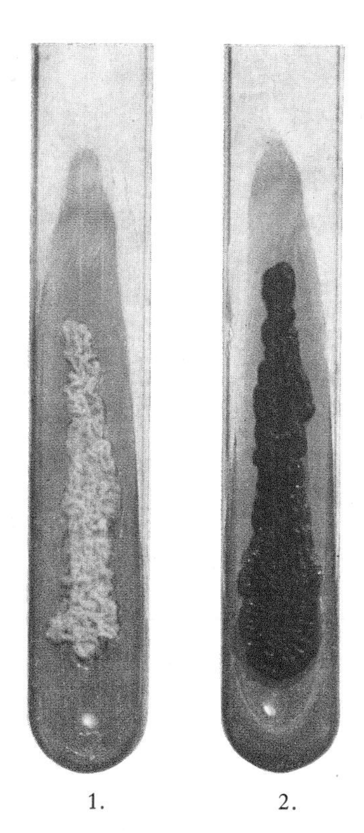

FIG. 150.

Stroke cultures of **non-pathogenic yeasts** on Sabouraud's maltose agar.

1. **Saccharomyces cerevisiæ,** the different strains of which are used in baking and brewing.
2. **Torula rubra** (**cryptococcus**) a common contaminant of culture media.

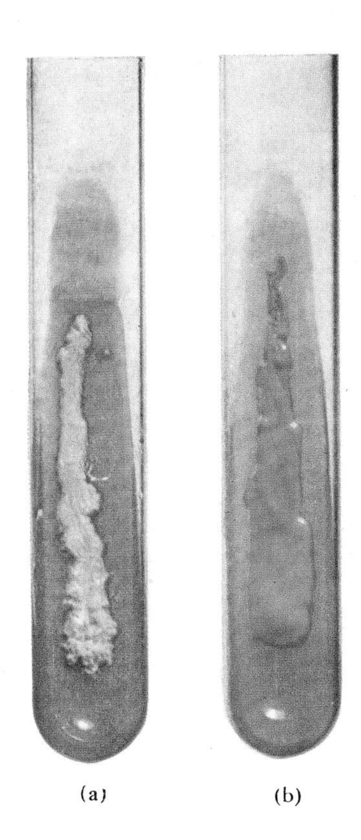

FIG. 151.

Stroke cultures of **pathogenic fungi** on Sabouraud's maltose agar.
(a) **Monilia albicans** the causative organism of " Thrush."
(b) **Torula histolytica** (**Cryptococcus hominis or neoformans**) the causative organism of **European Blastomycosis.**

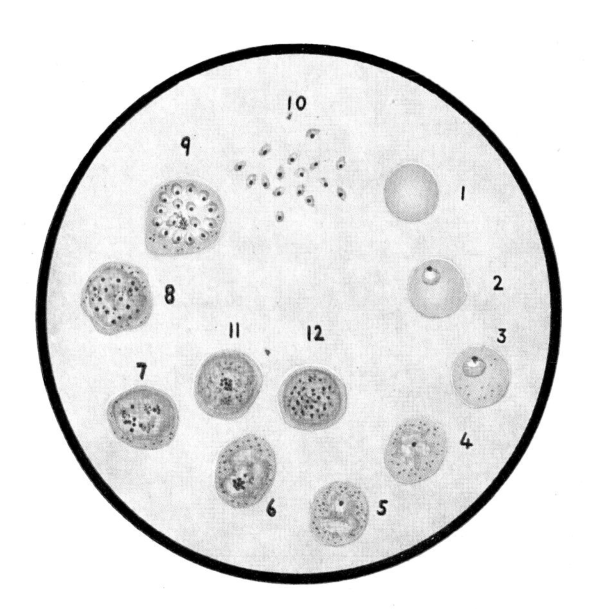

FIG. 152.

× **1000.** *Leishman's stain.*

The stages of **Schizogony (asexual cycle)** of **Plasmodium vivax** (the causative organism of **benign tertian malaria**) in the circulating red blood corpuscle.

1. Normal red blood corpuscle; as a rule no adherent merozoite seen.
2. Early trophozoite inside red cell.
3. Later trophozoite, "signet-ring" stage.

4-7. Increase in size of trophozoite; alterations in shape; protrusion of pseudopodia; deposit of golden-yellow pigment.

8. Schizont stage.
9. Segmentation of schizont to form rosette of sixteen merozoites with golden-yellow pigment in centre. Note gradual enlargement of the red blood corpuscle.
10. Liberation of merozoites after rupture of red-cell.
11. Macrogametocyte (female) } *see* **Sporogony,** Fig. 155.
12. Microgametocyte (male) }

Note that the red blood corpuscles in 3-9 show Schüffner's dots.

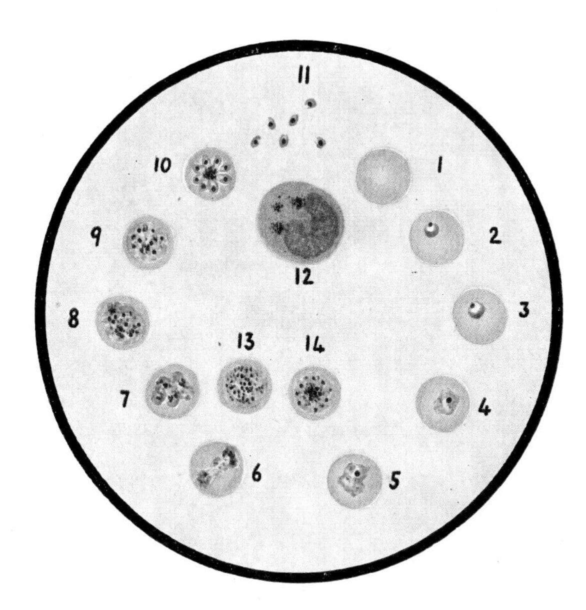

FIG. 153.

× **1000.** *Leishman's stain.*

The stages of **Schizogony (asexual cycle**) of **Plasmodium malariæ** (the causative organism of **benign quartan malaria**) in the circulating red blood corpuscle.

1. Normal red blood corpuscle; as a rule no adherent merozoite.
2-3. Early trophozoite stages :—rings.
4-7. Growing trophozoite showing amœboid movement and pseudopodia; abundant golden-brown or blackish pigment.
6. Characteristic " band " form of trophozoite.
8-9. Schizont stage.
10. Segmentation of schizont to form rosette of eight merozoites. Note that the red cell is not enlarged (cf., P. vivax).
11. Liberation of merozoites after rupture of red cell.
12. Phagocytosis of liberated pigment by large mononuclear cells of blood.
13. Macrogametocyte (female) } *see* **Sporogony,** Fig. 155.
14. Microgametocyte (male) }

Note the absence of Schüffner's dots and the dark-colour and larger size of pigment granules as compared with P. vivax and P. falciparum.

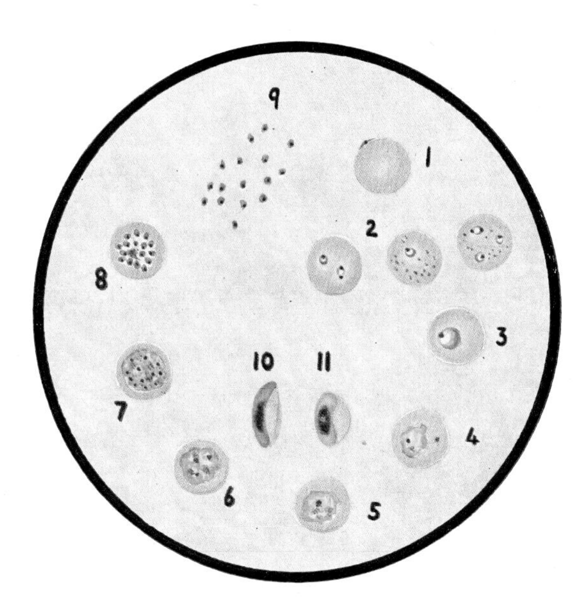

FIG. 154.

× **1000.** *Leishman's stain.*

The stages of **Schizogony (asexual cycle)** of **Plasmodium falciparum** (the causative organism of **malignant tertian malaria** in the red blood corpuscle).

Note that in this type of malaria only stages 1, 2, 3, 10 and 11 are in the circulating blood; the other stages occur in the red cells in the internal organs.

1. Red blood corpuscle frequently shows adherent merozoite.
2. Early trophozoites—note that more than one parasite may be seen in a single red cell; note also Maurer's dots.
3. Trophozoite—" signet-ring " stage.

4-6. Trophozoite increasing in size and showing golden-brown pigment.

7. Schizont.
8. Segmentation of schizont to form a large number of merozoites. Note rosette formation is not so symmetrical as in other forms of malaria and the merozoites are smaller in size.
9. Liberation of merozoites after rupture of red cell.
10. Macrogametocyte (female crescent) } characteristic of P. falciparum.
11. Microgametocyte (male crescent) }

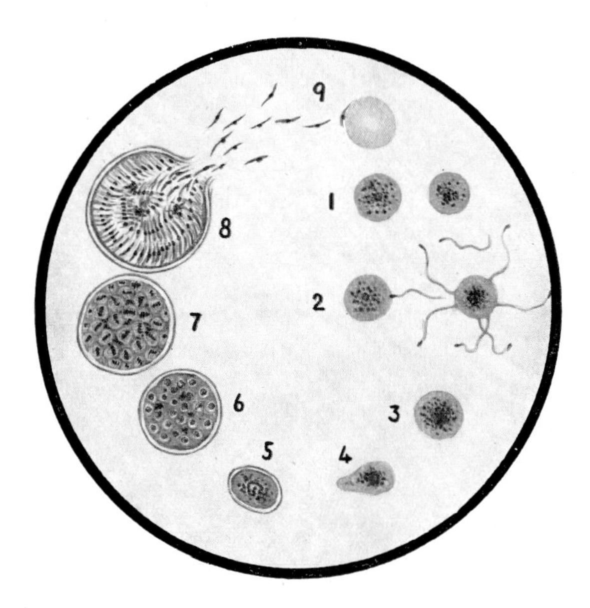

FIG. 155.

× **1000.** *Leishman's stain.*

The stages of **Sporogony**—the **sexual cycle** of the malaria parasites in the mosquito.

1. Macrogametocyte (female) and microgametocyte (male).
2. Microgametocyte showing exflaggelation, *i.e.*, extrusion of microgametes some of which penetrate the macrogametocyte to fertilize it.
3. Fertilized macrogamete—zygote or öökinete.
4. Zygote as it penetrates the stomach wall of mosquito.
5. Sporocyst in stomach wall of mosquito.
6. Sporoblasts inside sporocyst.
7. Transformation of sporoblasts into sporozoites.
8. Rupture of sporocyst and setting free of sporozoites, many of which invade the salivary gland of the mosquito and are injected into the human blood when the insect bites.
9. Sporozoite adhering to surface of human red blood corpuscle prior to entering the cell.

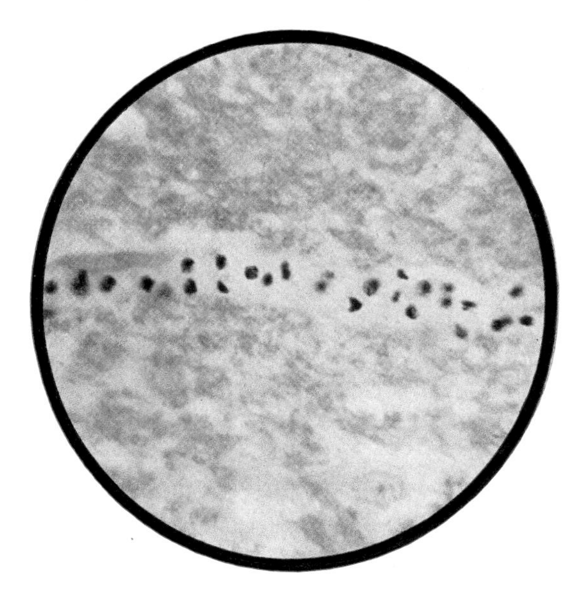

FIG. 156.

× **1000.** *Giemsa's stain.*

Section of brain from case of malignant tertian malaria showing cerebral vessel in which every red blood cell shows the deeply pigmented trophozoite of **Plasmodium falciparum.**

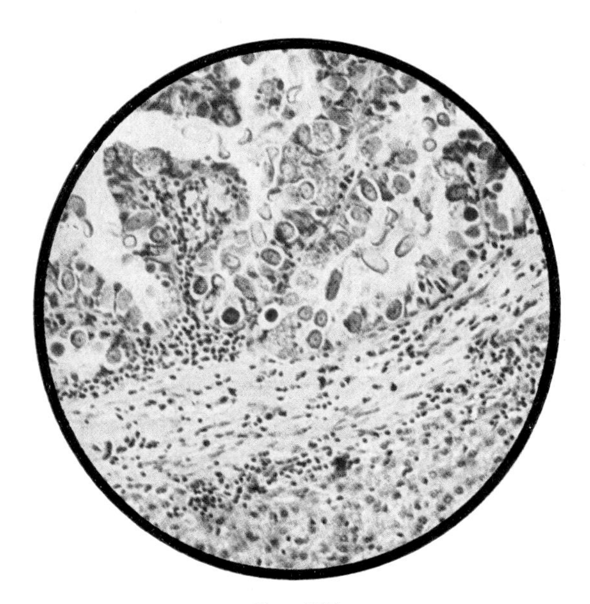

FIG. 157.

× **150.** *Hæmatoxylin and eosin stain.*

Section of rabbit's liver showing numerous large oval öocysts of **Coccidium cuniculi or oviforme (Eimeria stiedæ)** inside the proliferated epithelial cells of the bile-ducts. The öocyst measures 20-40μ long × 15-20μ broad and is the mature stage in sporogony of the parasite.

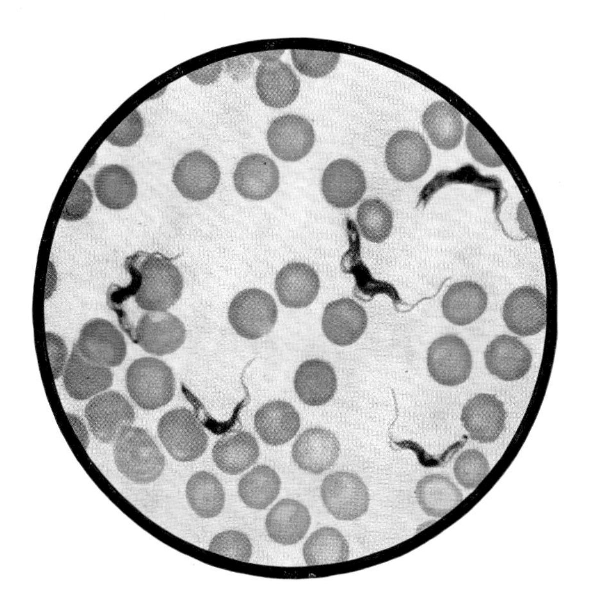

FIG. 158.

× **1000.** *Leishman's stain.*

Blood film of experimental mouse showing **Trypanosoma brucei.** Note the undulating membrane along the free margin of which the flagellum passes to project from the anterior end; the large trophonucleus in the centre and the smaller kinetonucleus (kinetoplast) at the posterior end. To estimate the length of the trypanosome compare with the red blood corpuscles (5-6μ in the mouse).

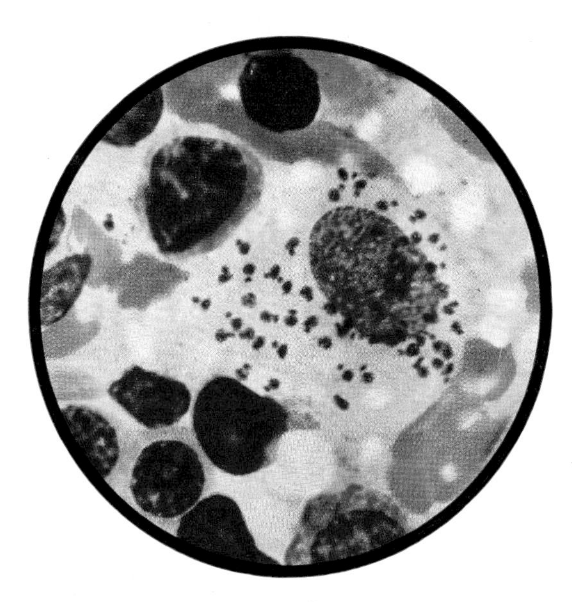

Fig. 159.

× **1000.** *Leishman's stain.*

Smear of bone marrow obtained by sternal puncture in case of **Kala-azar** showing **Leishmania donovani** in large numbers. Note the large macronucleus and the smaller blepharoplast; also variation in size of the parasite. (The intracellular position of the Leishmania can be seen.)

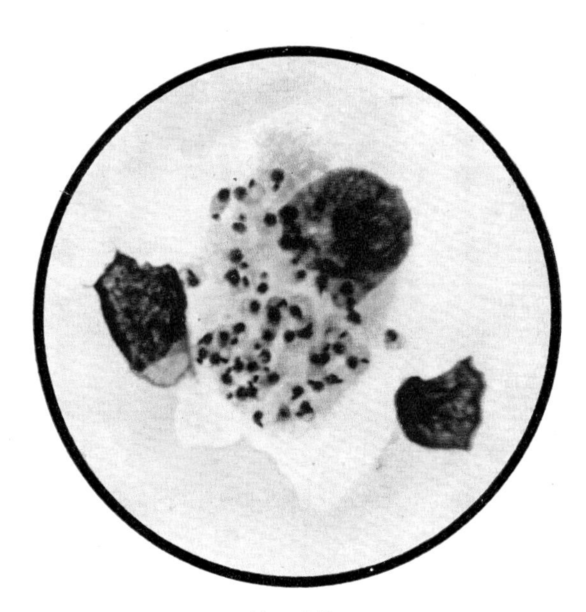

Fig. 160.

× **1000.** *Leishman's stain.*

Film of exudate from **Oriental sore** showing **Leishmania tropica.** Note its general resemblance to L. donovani. (The intracellular position of the parasites is well shewn in this illustration.)

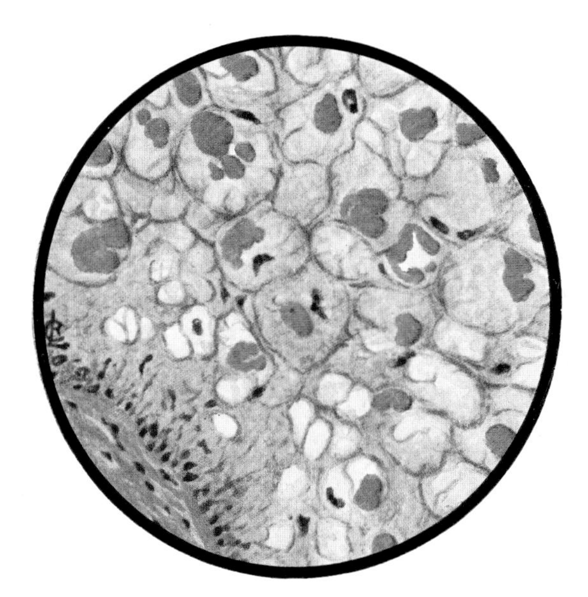

FIG. 161.

× **1000.** *Hæmatoxylin and eosin stain.*

Section of hen's skin showing the virus inclusion bodies (**Bollinger bodies**) of **Fowl-pox** inside the epithelial cells. Note their irregular shape and size and eosinophile character.

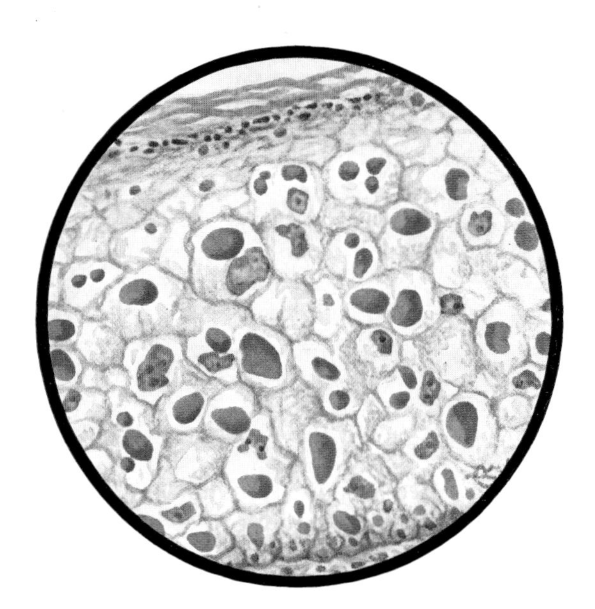

FIG. 162.

× **1000.** *Methylene blue and eosin stain.*

Section of skin from mouse's foot showing the virus inclusion bodies of **Ectromelia** inside the epithelial cells.

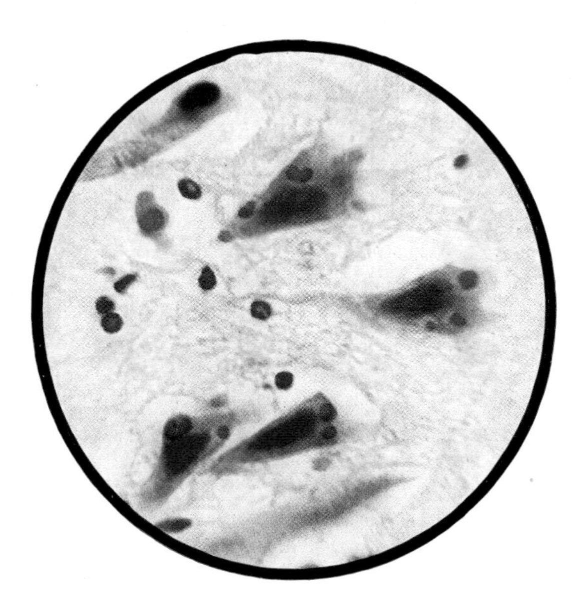

Fig. 163.

× **1000.** *Hæmatoxylin and alcoholic eosin stain.*

Section of hippocampus of brain of dog suffering from **Rabies** showing the large round and oval inclusion bodies (**Negri bodies**) which are diagnostic of the condition.

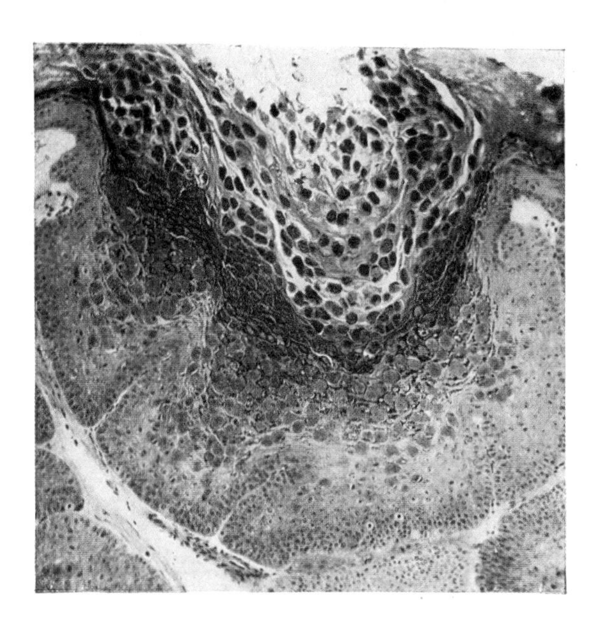

Fig. 164.

× **70.** *Hæmatoxylin and eosin stain.*

Section of **Molluscum contagiosum** lesion under low power showing large round and oval virus inclusion bodies (**molluscum or Henderson-Paterson bodies**) stained red inside the epithelial cells. These bodies gradually rise to the surface in the growing epithelial cells.

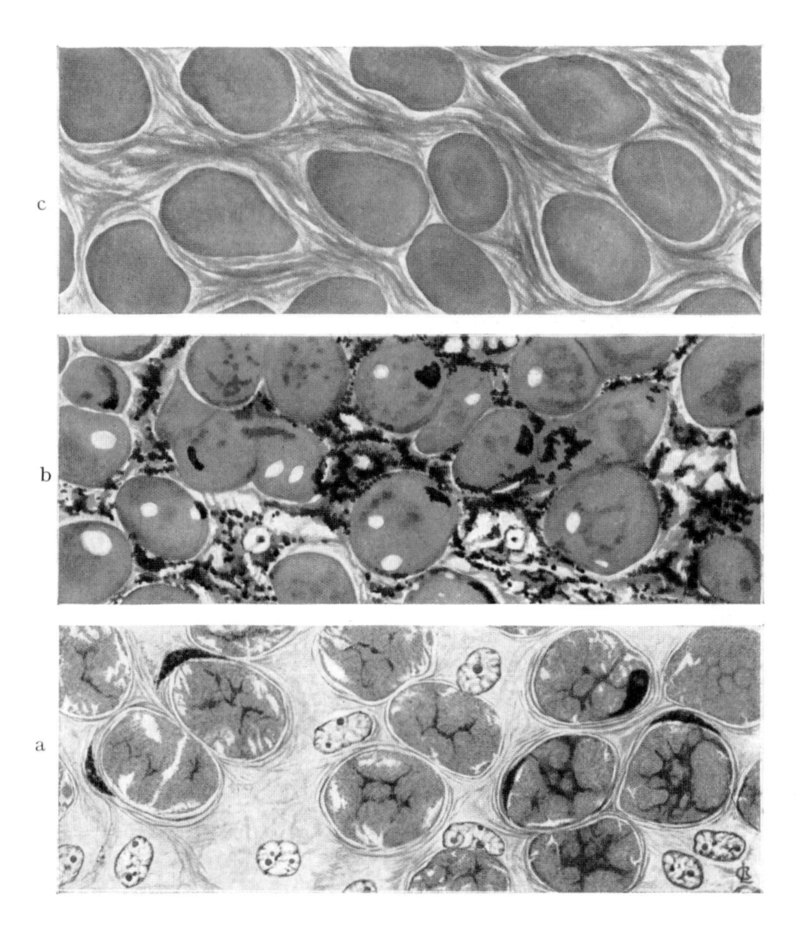

FIG. 165.

× **2000.** *Hæmatoxylin and eosin stain.*

Section of **Molluscum contagiosum** at three levels.

(a) About the middle of the Malpighian layer showing large inclusion bodies occupying the greater part of the epithelial cell and pushing the nucleus to one side so that it becomes flattened and crescentic in shape. Each inclusion body has a capsular membrane surrounding it and is filled with myriads of minute inclusion (Lipschutz) bodies stained red with eosin. The elementary bodies are grouped in irregular masses separated by trabeculæ which are continuous with the capsular membrane.

(b) A later stage of the molluscum bodies at the level of the Stratum granulosum. The capsular membrane and trabeculæ are now so dense that the elementary bodies are no longer visible. The white spots are bubbles of air inside the elementary body. The dark purple granular material is the hypertrophied keratohyalin of the stratum granulosum.

(c) Final stage of the inclusion body (Molluscum body) in the Stratum corneum.

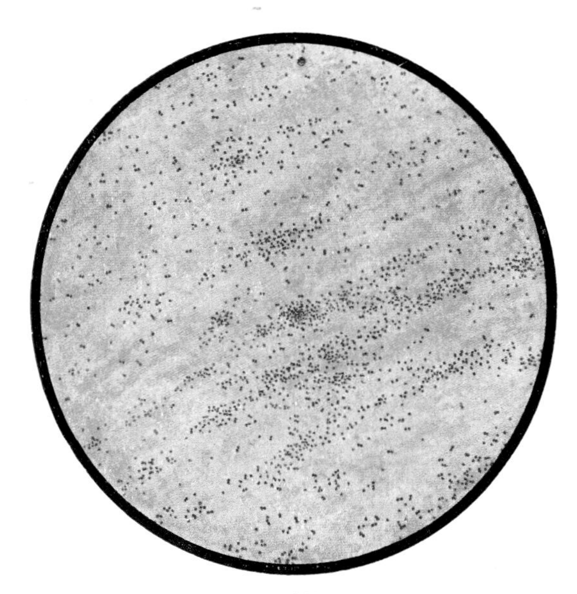

FIG. 166.

× **1000.** *Paschen's stain.*

Film made from a culture of **Vaccinia** virus in the developing hen egg. In making the film the cells have ruptured and liberated enormous numbers of elementary bodies (**Buist-Paschen bodies**). Note size (0·25μ) and frequent arrangement in pairs. A staphylococcus has been placed at the top of the film to show the comparative size.

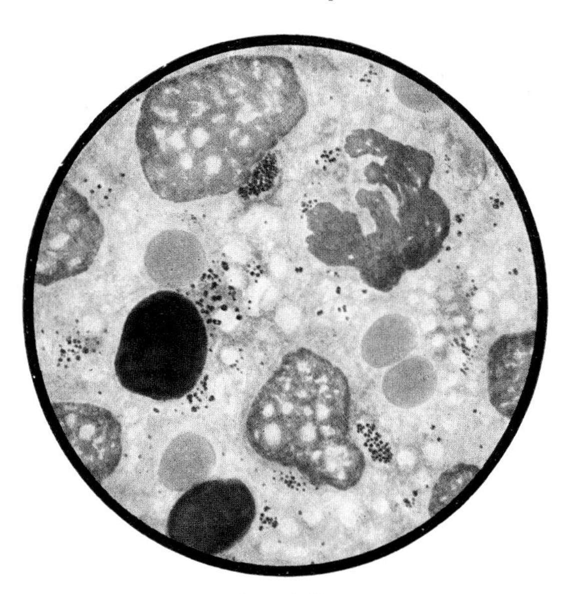

FIG. 167.

× **1000.** *Giemsa's stain.*

Film of mouse spleen showing the **Psittacosis** virus. The spleen was soft and diffluent and the nuclei of the cells enormously swollen. As the cells have all ruptured the intracellular position of the virus is not seen. The different stages of growth of the virus elementary bodies are seen the size varying from 0·3μ downwards. Two groups of the larger rounded forms are seen forming " morulæ " : large oval forms showing bipolar staining and very minute particules are also visible.

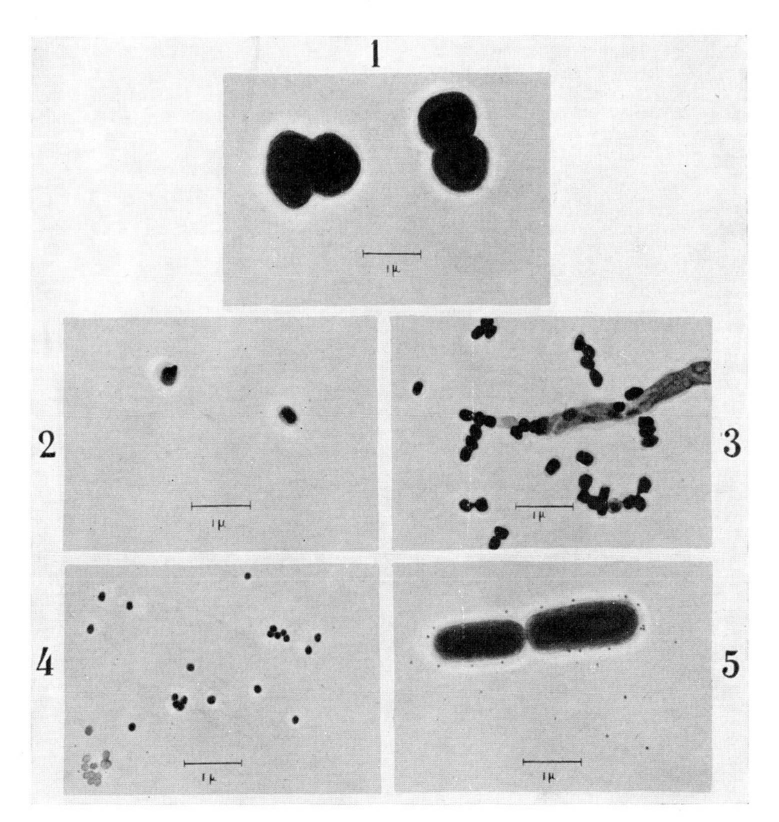

FIG. 168.

× **9000.**

A series of photographs taken with the **electron microscope** at a magnification of 9000 diameters to show the relative sizes of the different types of organism.

(1) Gonococcus (0·8-1μ). Two pairs of cocci are seen.
(2) Rickettsia prowazeki, 0·3μ.
(3) Elementary bodies of Vaccinia virus 0·25μ. Note that they are square cornered and slightly longer than broad.
(4) Elementary bodies of Influenza virus 0·1μ.
(5) Bacillus coli surrounded by " bacteriophage " particles, 0·03μ.

INDEX